With the permission of relatives, the names and photos of several deceased people have been included in this publication. All proceeds from the sale of this book return to Yalanji organisations to support ongoing land management and cultural projects.

Yalanji People of the Rainforest **Fire Management Book**

Dedication

This book is dedicated to all the Elders who contributed their stories, wisdom and knowledge, and to the memory of those who have passed on...

First published in Australia by **Little Ramsay Press 2004**
PO Box 4761, Cairns, Queensland, 4870, Australia
Phone: (07) 4055 1163
Email: ramsaypress@ozemail.com.au

The book is acknowledged as written by:
Rosemary Hill, Adelaide Baird, David Buchanan, Charlie Denman, Peter Fischer, Karen Gibson, Jimmy Johnson, Alma Kerry, George Kulka (Snr.), Eddie Madsen, Alec Olbar (Jnr.), Lizzie Olbar, Jack Pierce, Judy Shuan, Ena Shipton, Harry Shipton (Snr.), Jimmy Smith, Rene Sykes, Eileen Walker, Wilma Walker, Peter Wallace, Bobby Yerry, Dolly Yougie, Doreen Ball, Edward Barney, Raymond Buchanan, Ronald Buchanan, Harold Denman, Reuben Fischer, Roy Gibson, Leah Talbot, Elizabeth Tayley, Norman Tayley, Dawn Walker, Francis Walker, Kathleen Walker, Marilyn Wallace and Lily Yougie.

The book was translated by:
Doreen Ball, Eileen Walker, Francis Walker, Kathleen Walker, and Lily Yougie.

Graphic Design by Stephen Lane, Matthew Coghlan & Bob Withrington @ Mak Advertising.
Scans by Highscan, Cairns.
Printing by Everbest, China.

ISBN 0-9580984-1-7
Hill, R., *et al.* 2004. *Yalanji-Warranga Kaban. Yalanji People of the Rainforest Fire Management Book.*
Cairns: Little Ramsay Press.
I. Kuku-Yalanji (Australian people) - Social life and customs
II. Fire management rainforest

Acknowledgments:
For acknowledgements see page 11.

This project has been supported by:

CONTENTS

The Researchers *by Rosemary Hill*

Many people have contributed to this book. The idea of the book first came alive as part of collaborative fire research between *Yalanji* people and myself starting in 1995. Some of this research contributed to my doctoral thesis completed in 1998 with James Cook University. Both content and collaborative process has been reported on in the academic literature (see references pg 110).

The senior *Yalanji* traditional owners conducting the research were passionate about wanting to pass on their knowledge of country and fire to younger *Yalanji* people. Key senior co-researchers included Alma Kerry, George Kulka (Snr.), Peter Fischer, Harry Shipton (Snr.), Eileen Walker, Jack Pierce, Charlie Denman, Alec Olbar (Jnr.), Dolly Yougie, Bobby Yerry, Jimmy Johnson, Rene Sykes, Ena Shipton, and Wilma Walker. A little part of the wonderful stories of these people's lives are in the book. Peter Fischer in particular described to me the sort of book he wanted, with pictures, and written in *Yalanji* language. Adelaide Baird and David Buchanan, who worked alongside me as co-researchers at Wujal Wujal and Mossman respectively, also strongly supported the idea of a book for *Yalanji* people from the research.

The senior *Yalanji* people's idea of the book was a good one, but it needed to have the support of all *Yalanji* people. The first step in developing the book was taken in late 1999 when I went around talking to *Yalanji* people in Wujal Wujal, Mossman, and China Camp. Everyone was very enthusiastic about the book, so long as the right cultural protocols were followed to approve its content. The next step involved developing a joint submission between Wujal Wujal Aboriginal Community Council, Bamanga Bubu Ngadimunku, the Cape York Land Council and the Rainforest Cooperative Research Centre (CRC) for funding support from the Natural Heritage Trust (NHT). This submission laid out the cultural protocols that would be followed.

The funding submission was successful and we started the book project in 2001. The first stage in the cultural protocol was to invite all *Yalanji* people to a big meeting at Cape Tribulation in October 2001. At this meeting a Management Committee of *Yalanji* people was appointed to oversee the whole project. The Rainforest CRC agreed to provide the book project with an in-kind contribution of my time, and also granted further funding-the CRC's strong support and recognition of the importance of strengthening Indigenous peoples' knowledge systems was crucial throughout the project. In addition, the Australian Conservation Foundation supported my continuing involvement in the book as part of my job of Northern Australia Program Coordinator from 2003-ACF's interest and encouragement is greatly appreciated.

The Management Committee *by the Committee*

Roy Gibson, Harold Denman, David Buchanan, Raymond Buchanan, Edward Barney, Reuben Fischer, Ronald Buchanan, Elizabeth Tayley, Lizzie Olbar, Adelaide Baird, Marilyn Wallace, Norman Tayley, Eileen Walker, Dawn Walker and Doreen Ball accepted the nominations from the *Yalanji* meeting to be part of the Committee. We were not all able to attend all the meetings. Great sadness also came to our group when Dawn Walker passed away. After a while the Walker family asked Janice Walker to take her place. Jim Brooks from the Cape York Land Council was a corresponding member. The Management Committee met several times, and made all the decisions about the book. We held most of our meetings at Cape Tribulation, as the half-way point between Wujal Wujal and Mossman.

We took the Committee work very seriously, as getting the book right is important business for us. We asked Rosemary to write the first Plain English version, and Steven Nowakowski to be the photographer. We also appointed Leah Talbot, a *Yalanji* woman working at the University, to be our research assistant, and she helped with all the Committee work. We conducted more field work to get photos and information. The Committee asked the Wujal Wujal Language Group to translate the book. Mak Advertising was asked to do the graphic design and Karen Gibson to supply artwork. We made formal presentations of the draft book to public meetings held at Mossman and Wujal Wujal, and left a mock-up of the book in the communities for all interested people to review.

We made a second application to NHT (jointly between the same four organisations) for further funding to print the book. This second submission laid out the protocols for use of any funds generated by selling the book. Everyone agreed that all funds would return to the two *Yalanji* organisations, Bamanga Bubu Ngadimunku and Wujal Wujal Aboriginal Community Council, to support land and sea management, and language programs. We approved the final version to be printed by Everbest.

Above Left: *Field work at Wujal Wujal (Photo: R. Hill)*

Above Right: *Management Committee members at Cape Tribulation. From left- Edward Barney, Roy Gibson, Raymond Buchanan, Rosemary Hill, Kathleen Walker, Steven Nowakowski, Leah Talbot, Marilyn Wallace, Francis Walker, Doreen Ball and Eileen Walker.*

The Translators *by the Wujal Wujal Language Group*

Francis Walker, Eileen Walker, Lily Yougie, Doreen Ball, and Kathleen Walker started the Wujal Wujal Language Group with the assistance of the Wujal Wujal Aboriginal Community Council and Kate Prout in 1998. Our first project was to develop a new version of the *Kuku-Yalanji* Dictionary. Lynette Oakes had published a dictionary back in 1992 but it was hard to get and needed some corrections.

We all love working on *Yalanji* language books. It is hard to see so many of our young people not speaking the language properly. We feel more *Yalanji* language should be taught at school. We need more materials to help our young people learn language. *Yalanji* people are the experts on our language. If we have any doubts about words, or how to spell them, we talk around the community and with the elders.

We were very excited to be asked to translate the book. It was a big challenge for us because we hadn't done a whole book before. Francis is the Coordinator for our group. We shared out parts of the book, so our name appears beside the sections we each translated. Francis put it all onto the computer, and kept us all organised! She is on email too, so we were able to email our work to Cairns when it was finished. We are looking forward to doing more *Yalanji* books and materials for our young people, and the school.

The Photographer *by Steven Nowakowski*

I am really excited to be part of this book project. I was asked to take the photographs with a very strict condition that all the photographs belong to the *Yalanji* people. I believe over time these images will show future generations, both European and Indigenous, how rich, diverse and important traditional knowledge and culture is to this island home we call Australia.

I feel very privileged to have had the chance to step inside the *Kuku-Yalanji* culture and experience the true essence of traditional life. Above all else, my experiences with the *Yalanji* people have given me a new insight into the Australian bush, and what it can provide in terms of food and shelter. I have found that the *Yalanji* people's intimate knowledge of their respective lands to be extraordinary, and I am greatly indebted to have the opportunity to catch a glimpse of this wisdom.

As well as my photographs, the book also includes some photos taken by Rosemary Hill, Rupert Russell, Suzette Coates and some historical photos collected from the John Oxley Library and the Mason Family.

Formal Acknowledgements

We, the authors, artists, translators and photographers, would like to thank the following organisations for supporting this project over many years:
Australian Conservation Foundation Inc., Bamanga Bubu Ngadimunku Inc., Bama Rainforest Aboriginal Association (Bama Wabu) Inc., Balkanu Cape York Development Corporation, Cape York Land Council Inc., Cape York Natural Heritage Trust, Cooperative Research Centre for Tropical Rainforest Ecology and Management (Rainforest CRC), James Cook University School of Tropical Environment Studies and Geography (TESAG), Wet Tropics Managment Authority, Wujal Wujal Aboriginal Community Council Inc.

We would also like to acknowledge the following people who contributed to the book in many different ways by attending meetings, contributing information, or just general help. We hoped we have not missed anyone.

Yalanji people and family members:-

Mr Bobby Ball
Mr Jacky Ball
Mrs Jenny Ball
Mr Jimmy Baird
Mr Kevin Baird
Mrs Lorraine Baird
Mrs Polly Baird
Mr Robert Baird
Ms Cecilia Barry
Mr George Bremer
Mrs Aggie Burchill
Mr Jay Burchill
Mr Alec Creek
Mrs Marie Creek
Mr Joseph Cummins
Mr Anthony Davis
Mr George M. Davis
Mr Billy Denman
Mrs Eva Denman
Ms Laurel Denman
Mrs Katie Diamond
Ms Donna Henning
Mr Bamboo Friday
Mr Cedric Friday
Mr Colin Friday
Mrs Gladys Friday
Mrs Ruby Friday
Mr Daryl Gibson
Mr Jimmy Henry
Mr George Kulka (Jnr.)
Mr Michael Kulka
Mr Alwyn Lyall
Mrs Annie Madsen
Mrs Rhoda McAllistair
Mr Darren Nandy
Mr Patrick Nandy
Mrs Telida Nandy
Mrs Emily Olbar
Mr Jimmy Olbar
Mr Gerhardt Pearson
Mr Noel Pearson
Mr Raymond Pierce
Mr Rodney Riley
Mr Edward Roberts
Mrs Mabel Salt
Mr McGinty Salt
Mr Alfred Smith
Mr Herbert Smith
Mr Andy Solomon
Mrs Christine Solomon
Mr David Solomon
Mrs Elizabeth Talbot
Mr Desmond Tayley
Mr Bennett Walker
Mrs Mary Wallace
Ms Agnes Walker
Mr Henry Walker
Ms Janice Walker
Mr Linc Walker
Mr Stanton Walker
Mr Conrad Yeatman
Mrs Barbara Yougie
Mr Youngaman Yougie

Others:-

Mr Richie Ahmat
Dr Chris Anderson
Ms Sharon Anderson
Mr Jim Brooks
Dr Jill Carstairs
Ms Suzette Coates
Mr Mike Graham
Dr Peter Griggs
Dr Graham Harrington
Mr Nigel Hedgecock
Mr Tony Irvine
Mr Bruce Lawson
Mr John Madsen
Professor Helene Marsh
Mrs Anne Mason
Mr Paul Mason
Professor Geoff McDonald
Mr Dwayne Mundraby
Mr Vince Mundraby
Ms Melissa Nursey-Bray
Ms Kylie Pursche
Mr Bruce Rampton
Mr Ray Rex
Ms Cheryl Roberts
Dr Dermot Smyth
Ms Lisa Stagoll
Ms Marita Stinton
Professor Nigel Stork
Associate Professor Steve Turton
Associate Professor Peter Valentine
Ms Diane Ward
Mr Russell Watkinson
Mr Terry Webb
Mr Ray Wood

Kaban Jakalbamun

Ngalkalji, madjaji, jukar, dulngkuburr, wuburrdurr wunay kalbaliku karangkaldarr Mossman, Annandarr wawubajanga bubu bural Nganjin Naka-Nakamun Yalanjinga bamanga. Ngana yaluy ngadimunkuku. Kuku jawun karrandamun Nganjin Naka-Nakamun Yalanji bama mankurruburrur yilkinga dungan dungay wuburrdurr jankanga bunjuruburr. Ngana Yalanji bama nyiku yaluy kujil kujil junkurrjiku ngujakuramunkuku balkan nyiku nyikumunkuda. *- Translated by Doreen Ball*

Above: *Yalanji families Ena Shipton, Adelaide Baird and Emily Olbar, walking Cedar Bay Beach. (Photo: R. Hill)*

"Kuku-Yalanji" nganjinangakuda Yalanji warra kuku. Nganjinanga kanbalanga bamanga kuku walindurr.

- Translated by Lily Yougie

Yalanji warra bama nganjin wubulku jawun-karraji, yamba nganjin maja nganjinanunku bubuku. Bama wanya maja yinyangka bubuku janaku balkawaka. Bama yinyamun bubumun janaku maja-karra. Yundu binalmangka yunungku Yalanji munku bubuku, yundu yunu bubu warrmbabunga yinyamun yunu jawun-karra warrmbabunga yala bubu yununku wawumalda.

- Translated by Kathleen Walker

Note from the Translators:
Please note that there is not a direct correspondence between English and *Yalanji* words.
These translations take the whole meaning and put it into *Yalanji* language.

Introduction

The tropical rainforests, beaches, reefs, and mountain ranges stretching along the coast between Mossman and the Annan River are the homelands of Eastern *Yalanji* people *(bama)*. We have been here since the beginning in the dreaming. Stories of the lives of past generations of Eastern *Yalanji* bama are held in every mangrove inlet, in the roaring torrents and giant mountain boulders, and in the silent sliding streams. We *Yalanji bama* are still here today and hold strongly to our Law, culture and language in building for the future.

Above: *Jeremy Cooktown, a Mossman boy enjoying a day at Cape Kimberley.*

Overleaf: *Weary Bay*

"Kuku-Yalanji" literally means speakers of *Yalanji* language. There are several dialects within this language.

Yalanji bama are related to each other and to different parts of our lands through our customary law. Only those people with the right connections to a particular place can speak for that country, for that place. The tract of country belonging to our particular family group is known as our "clan estate".

To know your role and your place in *Yalanji* society, you must know your country, your clan estate and your kin.

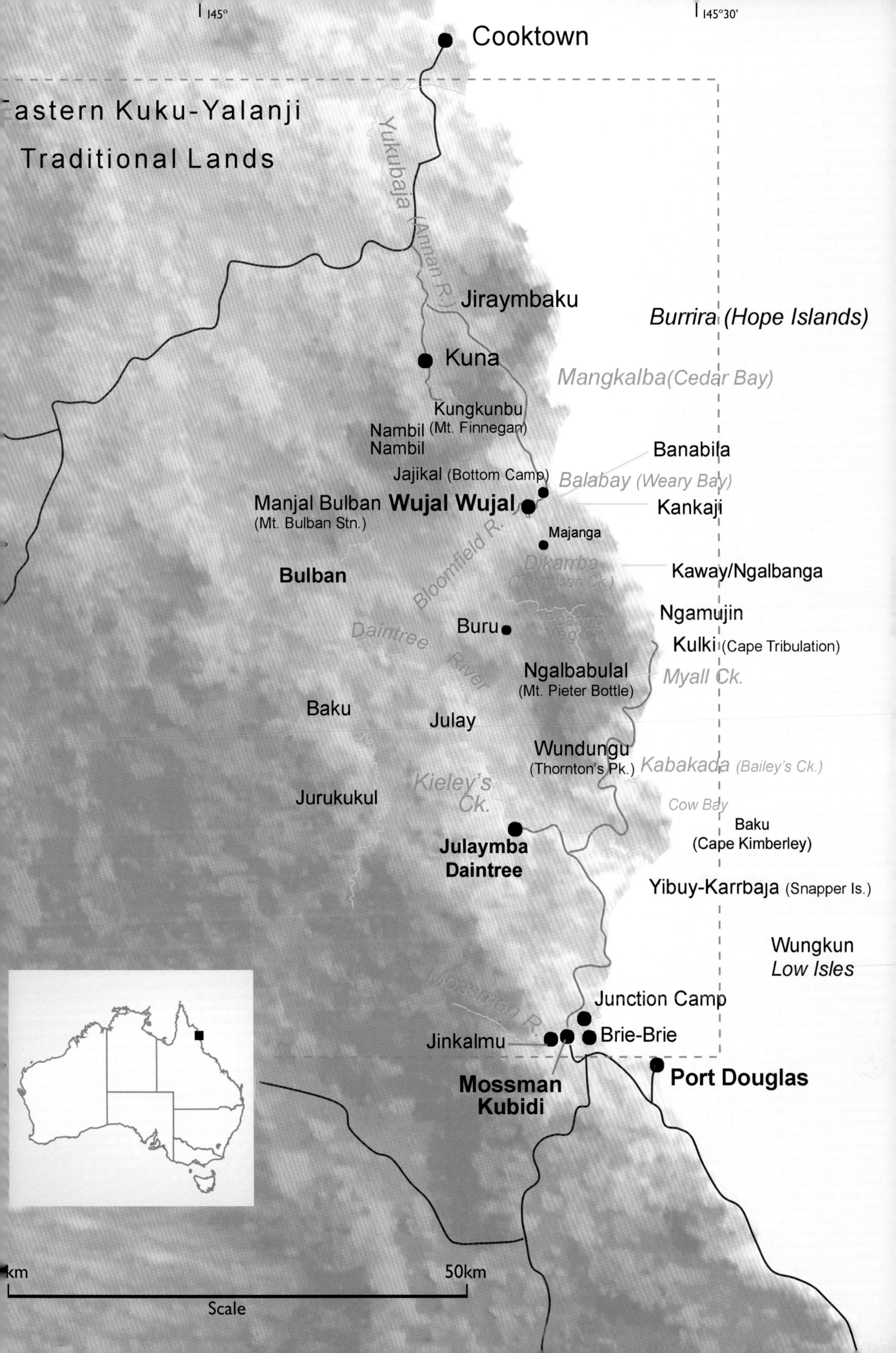

145°
145°30'
Cooktown
Eastern Kuku-Yalanji
Traditional Lands
Yukubaja (Annan R.)
Jiraymbaku
Burrira (Hope Islands)
Kuna
Mangkalba (Cedar Bay)
Kungkunbu (Mt. Finnegan)
Nambil Nambil
Banabila
Jajikal (Bottom Camp)
Balabay (Weary Bay)
Manjal Bulban
(Mt. Bulban Stn.)
Wujal Wujal
Kankaji
Majanga
Bloomfield R.
Dikarrba
(Thompson Ck.)
Kaway/Ngalbanga
Bulban
Ngamujin
Buru
Daintree River
Kulki (Cape Tribulation)
Ngalbabulal
(Mt. Pieter Bottle)
Myall Ck.
Baku
Julay
Wundungu
(Thornton's Pk.)
Kabakada (Bailey's Ck.)
Kieley's Ck.
Jurukukul
Cow Bay
Baku
(Cape Kimberley)
Julaymba
Daintree
Yibuy-Karrbaja (Snapper Is.)
Wungkun
Low Isles
Junction Camp
Mossman R.
Jinkalmu
Brie-Brie
Mossman
Kubidi
Port Douglas
km
50km
Scale

Waybala kadan Yalanjinga bubungu nyiku-nyiku 19th centurynga. Jana kadan nubingka kulji, juku mirrbangku, bijilima, yalarrku dakal-dakal manin, jana mayi bungku-jaba nandan, jana yalarrku bayan wubul janaymanin. Waybala maja-maja kuku jurril dajin bamanda. Yamba nganjin Yalanji- warra bama junkurr janan nganjinangka bubuku, nganjinanga kuku junkurrji, nganjin kuku ngujakuramu kari bawan. Nyiku nganjin balkan-balkaway bubuku nganjinandamunku.

- Translated by Eileen Walker

Top Left: *Mossman resident Lorna Shuan tends to her garden within the community.*

Top Middle: *Kuku-Yalanji dancers led by David Buchanan perform at the Laura Cultural Festival.*

Top Right: *Wujal Wujal* community, situated between Cairns and Cooktown, is home to around 500 *Kuku-Yalanji* people.

Nyiku 3000 Nganjin Naka-Nakamun Yalanji Bama bundanday Mossman, Wujal Wujal, kanbal jawun-karra bunday ngami-ngami bubungu. Kanbal Eastern Yalanji bama bunday kala-kalbay bada Cairns, Canberra yindu- yindumbu bubungu. Nganjin kanbal jawun-karra bubungu kala-kalbay bunday yamba nganjinanga wawu yaluyku nganjinandaku bubungu, jawun-karranji.

- Translated by Francis Walker

Waybala, non-Aboriginal people, first started to come to the *Yalanji* homelands during the latter part of the 19th century. They came for gold and tin, to extract red cedar, beche-de-mer and pearl shell, and to establish sugar cane farms and towns. The *Waybala* government forced many bad policies on the *bama*. Even so, we *Yalanji bama* have kept our connection with our country, and we have kept our language, our Law, and culture alive throughout the time since first *waybala* occupation. We are still fighting to have our rights to our land and our culture recognised and respected.

Today some 3000 Eastern *Yalanji* people live in Mossman, *Wujal Wujal* and other small towns scattered throughout our homelands. Other Eastern *Yalanji* people live away from home, in Cairns, Canberra and many other places. Even when away from home, we still hold our connections and obligations to our land and our people.

Top Left: *Cedric Friday dot paints intricate designs on bark.*

Top Middle: *Dot painting up close - precision painting.*

Top Right: *Kirsty Burchill at a cultural camp near Cape Kimberley.*

Left: *Roaring Meg Creek.*

Top Right: *Edward Barney holding traditional axes.*

Bottom Right: *Scrub Turkey (diwan).*

Peter Wallace nyulu kuku Yalanji bama bundanday Wujal Wujal. Peter kuku junkurrji balkaway, bubuku, junjuy-junjuyngku ngulkurr bungangka. Nyubun junjuy nyulu nyajingka, yinyangka nganjinanga ngujakura junkurrjiman. Peterangka balkan:

Ngana bama jakalbamun. Yanyu bubu ngananga wubul junjuy-junjuynji, bambay ngulkurrbanka, mayi/minya jirray, junjuy-junjuy jilbaka. Nganjin binal bubu kujinka ngulkurrduku. Kulji, Juku, minya, dikal yalarrku nganjinanga maja (20 June 2001, Wujal Wujal).

- Translated by Doreen Ball

Ngujakuramungku Yalanji-warra bamangka ngalku wuljaljidaku wajul-wajun jikan jirakal dakalbaja.

-Translated by by Francis Walker

Top Left: *Roaring Meg Creek.*

Top Right: Peter Wallace aims to keep culture alive.

Peter Wallace is a *Yalanji* traditional owner who lives in Wujal Wujal. Peter plays a major role in land rights, community development and in working for a better future. One of his aims is to keep culture alive through education. Peter explains:

We are the first native people here. This country is our resource for medicines, for hunting and making weapons. We understand where our obligation lies to manage our country. Rocks, trees, animals and birds are also culture to Aboriginal people (20 June 2001, Wujal Wujal).

Fire management is an important part of *Yalanji* people's rights and responsibilities to our country.

Ngalku Yalanji-warranga bubuku

Ngalku Yalanji-warranga kuku, kararr, jikan wajul-wajunku madja, bural kidanka. Nganjinaga bubu darrirbunganka. Nganjin ngalku nyajil milka-bujarmalda nganjinanka Yalanji-warranka jawun karranka. Lizzie Olbar junkurrji jalunji jalbu nyulu ngadibajaku kuku yirrkan bubuku Yalanji-warranka. Nyulu kuku yirrkay nganawunku bubuku. Nyulu wanjabu dungay. Lizzie nyulu binal bajaku jukaraka, dulngkuku yala bada wangkar jalundurr. Lizzieangka balkan:

Top Left: *Ngalku is the Yalanji word for vegetation fires, for burning the bush. (Photo R. Russell)*

Top Right: *Fire within Yalanji country.*

Baya nganangku bamangaku. Nganjinangaku wajul-wajunku mayi. Yarkinmun burakanganka kunjirr yamba-yamba. Baya bamangaku ngadimunku bana baya. Baya kari, bana kari ngana bama yaluy wularida nyiku.

Ngana baya wajul junjuy-junjuyngku. Kanbal juku wumbul-bungal danda manil artifactsmunku, kalkaka, baluruku, yiki-yikimunku. Yala Tarzanangka mumbarabuku dandiku kujin ngadingkaku.

Wunbaka nganjin juku nyanda daray manil wunbaji juku nyubun wunbaku nyajin kari wubulku juku wajul buban baya kubuji mawal kanganka (28 May 1996, Jajikal). *- Translated by Doreen Ball*

Fire in the Yalanji World

Ngalku is the *Yalanji* word for vegetation fires, for burning the bush. *Ngalku* is very important in caring for country. Other aspects of fire also hold deep meaning and value for *Yalanji* people. Lizzie Olbar is a strong *Jalunji*[1] woman, who has fought for *Yalanji* land rights, and speaks up for our country wherever she goes. Lizzie has deep knowledge and connection to the beaches, reefs and coastal estates in the *Yalanji* world. She explains:

Top Left: *Wukay being prepared over fire.*

Top Right: *Fire is used to make a tar for binding.*

Fire is an important thing in bama's life. We use it for cooking mayi and for having ceremonies. Fire was the main source in bama life, second to water. Fire and water. Without the fire and the water, nobody would be here today.

We use fire for many purposes. A certain tree is heated over fire to produce a tar for making artefacts like spears, for making woomeras and didgeridoos. It's like Tarzan's grip, it stays on the bindings forever.... When old people go for a paddle, they get a turtle, they make a little bush fire, and you see the smoke, oh, they go, turtle all right.

For honey....we chop down a tree for honey, just one where we see the bee, not the whole lot, and make just enough little fire to smoke the tree and get the bees out. (28 May 1996, Jajikal).

[1] *Jalunji* are a sub-group of Yalanji people with special connection to the sea.

Left: *A storm gathers off Cape Tribulation (Kulki).*

Yamba-Yamba bamadamun yarkinmun. Jana yamba-yamba kujil kija wubul. Yamba-yamba bayanga burakal. Yinyamun wambajida jawun karrangada dajil. Yalanji-warra jalbu-jalbu ngungjil dirkabunganya walu julngkajinya mungkanga mandi-mandi yijarrinya.

- Translated by Lily Yougie

Ngadiku Yalanji bamangka jarramali kunjanya kuliji. Jalun marrkabunganka, Jana dingkar marri-marringka baya wajunya kubukal wurar birra kangka yijarrinya bayanga. Ngalku ngami-ngamiman yinya binga-binga marri-marri kula wunka badi kuda. Yinyamum ngalku kabangka nyunilda.

- Translated by Kathleen Walker

Above: *Calm seas near Hope Island. (Photo: R. Hill)*

Overleaf: *Early morning light on the Bloomfield River.*

The warming ceremony is conducted after people have passed away. All their belongings are put away until a certain time has passed. They are then taken out and warmed on the fire before being shared out with the family. During mourning of a death in the past, *Yalanji* people would crush charcoal to coat their faces and hair as a sign of respect.

In the old days, *Yalanji* people had rituals for troublesome fire and weather conditions. To calm rough, windy conditions on the sea, senior men would conduct a ceremony and produce smoke by placing green leaves from a special tree or the wild grape vine on the top of a fire. When a large fire threatened the community, a rainmaker would sing up a big storm, a big rain to put out the fire.

FIRE IN THE YALANJI WORLD

Nyujakuramun Kuku Ngalkuku

Ngalku bubungu wanyurrinku wajun bamanda yirmbalba. Wanyangka bamangka baya wajul bamanda majandaku babajika nguba yirmbal. Bakakiri ngadiku nyulu bamanka majaman nyulu bamanda jawunkarranda yalaman yurra waybala nyajil yalamaka baya kari waju:

Top Left: Peter Fischer, senior Law man. (Photo: R. Hill)

Top Right: Robert Baird, also a senior *Yalanji* Law man. (Photo: R. Hill)

Kuku-Yalanji bama nganjin kari dungay baya wajul, nganjin bama babaji yinyamunkuku ... ngayu maja ngaykuwunku bubuku, yundu kaday ngaykunwunbu bubungu baya wajul, ngayu yunin kunil, kari jurrilmal, ngayu yunun kalkabu damal, ngayu yunun yarkinkaku kunil. *- Translated by Eileen Walker.*

Kanbal yirmbal bural baya kari waju, yinya bural balu warra-waju. Binda Buyun, nyulu wulanda, nyulu maja Jalunjinku, nyulu binalbajaku kuku ngujakuramunku.

Nyulu balkan kuku wanjarr jana dingkar marri-marri ngadi-ngadiku baya wajun bubungu yirmbalba. Ngana kari waju, Ngana kari janjarrika, Bama yinyanmunku yala dingkar marri-marriku, ngarrbal bama kari yubakaday (29 November 1995, Wujal Wujal).

- Translated by Francis Walker.

Customary Law and Fire

Management of fires on country happens under customary Law in *Yalanji* society. Traditional owners of a clan estate, and other family members, have authority for making decisions about fires. Bobby Yerry is a senior traditional owner who passed away recently. He was an outstanding community leader for many years, and served as Chairperson of the Wujal Wujal Aboriginal Community Council for a decade. He explains how *Yalanji* people must have permission to light fires:

Top Left: Edward Barney and Roy Gibson.

Top Right: Alec Olbar at Cedar Bay where burning must follow strict customary Law.

(Photo: R. Hill)

Kuku-Yalanji people, we can't go ahead and just light a fire, we got to wait for the right people.... I'm a boss for my county, if you're coming into my country and lighting a fire, I'll kill you, no muck around, spear, I'll kill you! (30 April 1996, Zig Zag homestead).

Some cultural sites need to be protected from fire, and others need to be burnt only with the right ceremony. Alma Kerry was a very knowledgeable *Jalunji* elder. Alma kept many traditional stories and cultural practices alive. She explains the role of senior men in fire management of one important cultural site:

We can't burn it, we can't touch it, it has to be bama from there, has to be initiated men, no-one else can go near it
(29 November 1995, Wujal Wujal).

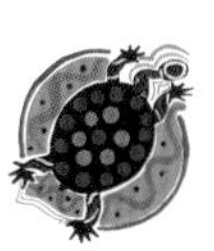

Kanbalba Marri-Marringa Kuku Ngujakuramun

Yanyu kuku kabanba Yalanji- warra marri-marri binga-binga yalarrku kamba-kambanga ngujakuramun, jana kanbal wulanda. Yalanji- warranga binga-binga, kamba-kambanga maja-majakuda, janakuda kuku yirrkay nyiku-nyiku kuku ngujakuramun ngana kari milka wulay. Yanyu kuku kanbalda Yalanji-warra binga-binga kamba-kambanga kuku dajin Ngalkuku. *- Translated by Francis Walker*

Kwinyala
George Kulka (Snr.)
(Photo R.Hill)

Kwinyala

Kwinyala balkajin Burungu. Nyulu yinyayku bundandan yununji jawun-karranji Kuku Yalanji-warranji. Warruku, Kwinyala workman waybalanji kulji mujal-mujan jananji, nyulu kari milka-wulan nyunuwunku nyujakuraka, jilbaka, warrmaka. Kwinyala jurrkijin naka Julaymba, yinyay kulji jirraymalman, nyulu kukuku walkandamunku binalman, nyulu bungku-jaba nyandan, yinyamun workmanijin farm-munbu. Yinyamun Kwinyala nyunguwungku bubuku kuku yirrkan, kari milka wulan ngujakuramunku, nyulu bamanka manun-manun. Nyulu kadan-baja 1990s, bayan nyunga janaymanin nyununbuku bubungu Burunguku.Kwinyala nyiku kuku wabam bubuku ngujakuramun wawurr-wawurrku. Nyulu yalaman:

Bama binal nganjinanga ngujakuramunku, kari yinya bawa,yala yirmbal... bubuku yundu junjuy-junjuy kuji ngulkurrduku nyuluku majangka balkan, jana-wunku bubuku, yala minya jarrabina,kadar, kurranji... Yalarrku kuji juku,junjuy-junjuy bubungu... ngalku buban waju karirrku yalbay, kari ngalku waju wungariji, mayi yam wajunji, yala juku wajuji... Waybalanga ngananga bama ngujakuramun kuku nyakaku (19 June 1996, Buru).

- Translated by Kathleen Walker

Some Senior *Ngalku* Law/Lore Holders

This book is based on the knowledge, wisdom, and stories shared by many senior *Yalanji* men and women, some of whom have since passed away. In *Yalanji* society, older people are the custodians of the Law (rules about behaviour) and the Lore, the knowledge system underpinning the Law. Here we briefly tell the stories of some *Yalanji* elders, and their insights about *ngalku*.

George Kulka (Snr.)

George Kulka was born at *Buru*, China Camp, and lived there with all the bama speaking *Yalanji* language. As a young boy, George worked collecting tin for the miners, while continuing to follow the *bama* Law, and the life of ceremonies, hunting and gathering. George moved to Daintree when the mining became more industrialised, learnt English and took up cane cutting and other farm work. George and his wife Annie had six children together. In later life, George was revered for his cultural knowledge, irrepressible humour and gentle wisdom. He moved back to *Buru* in the 1990s and built a house on his own beautiful country for the last years. George shared his extensive ecological and management knowledge with grace and enthusiasm:

Bama, knows our law, don't want to lose that, and our sacred things... native title, you're still looking after what the nature made, native things that belong to this country, tree climbing kangaroo, or wallaby, or cassowary... look after trees and things, country... to burn the grass, just a good fire, not to destroy anything, not in the real dry time, it might kill some yam, and kill the trees... white man gotta understand the bama law too (19 June 1996, Buru).

Top Right: *Roaring Meg Falls.*

Bottom Right: *George Kulka (Snr.) at home at China Camp. (Photo: R. Hill)*

Peter Fischer
(Photo R.Hill)

Challa/Jinkarr

Challa/Jinkarr balkajin Burungu, jakalbamunku ngawamunku yanyu century. Challa/Jinkarr nyungu bama burri, ngawamunku. Challa/Jinkarr jurrkijin naka Julaymba dungan warruku workman Frank Fischeranji. Nyulu mala work-bajaku workmanjin dairy farmburr, juku nyandal-nyandan, yinyamun bungku-jaba nyandan, yala yinyamun nyulu mara nyulkurr-bajaku jana majanka nyunun maja-bungan "Chop -Chop machine" bungku-jabangka. Challa/Jinkarr nyungu manyarr Polly bulanga kangkal-kangkal 13 bala. Challa/Jinkarr jurrkijin nyunguwunbuku wurrangku nyuluku balkajin kadan baja 1991. Nyulu bayan ngaran junjuy-junjuynji solar power system yalarrku composting toilet. Bama ngarrbal-ngarrbal waybal-waybal kaday Burungu, Jana Challa/Jinkarrnda kaday kukungu milka-janjanay, nyulu binal-baja kuku ngujakuramun. Challa/Jinkarrangka balkan:

Ngayu wawu jirray bajaku bubuku. Ngayu wawu kujinka bubu. Ngayu ngaykungunduku miyildaku nyajinka bubu wanjarrmalmal dungan-dungay jakalba nyuba kudamundu dungan-dungay. Bamakuda bundandarin ngadi-ngadiku. Ngalkubu buyun damal mawal. Ngayu wawu kari ngalkuku, Ngayu wawu jirray wunbaka. Jiba wula wula bajaku wunba (6 December 1995, Roaring Meg).

- Translated by Eileen Walker

Above: Peter walking his country. (Photo: R. Hill)

Peter Fischer

Peter was born at China Camp, *Buru*, in the early part of this century. *Challa* is his proper Aboriginal name, given to Peter at birth. Peter moved to Daintree as a boy to live and work with his step-father, Dick Fischer. He worked hard all his life in dairy farming, mining, clearing scrub but mostly in the sugar industry, where he gained a formidable reputation as the "chop-chop machine" of cane cutting. Peter and his wife Polly had thirteen children. In the 1980s Peter successfully participated in legal action to protect his traditional country, *Buru*, from mining. Peter is a strong advocate and continues to work for recognition of *bama* Law, culture, land and native title rights. Peter returned to live near his birth place in 1991, where he has built his own house complete with solar power system and composting toilet. Peter's inspirational wisdom and extensive knowledge of his culture and language attracts a constant stream of visitors to *Buru*. Peter explains:

I love the country, I like to look after the country.... my eye can see how the country is going forward, or going back.... that's the Aboriginal way of living in the early time. Fire can destroy a lot of native bees, I don't like bush fire because I like my honey, lovely honey (6 December 1995, Roaring Meg).

Charlie Denman

Burra

Charlie Denman balkajin, yalbayman Green Hill Stationba. Yinyamun jurrkijin Cooktown juma Julaymba. Charliemu ngamu Yalanji wulbuman nyulu Buruku, nyungundumun nyulu binalmal junjuy-junjungku yamunku barkamunku jungkaka, baduruku bubu, yala jilbaka bubu Burungu. Charliemu ngamu binga jawun Dabu. Nyungu nganjan Walarr. Charlieanka ngadibajaku bulki wundil wundin. Laura Station yarra Buruburr, bada Julaymba Mossman Butchering Companyanga. Milka bujarku Charlie wulan nyiku-nyiku. Nyulu balkan bamanda bayaka managementmunku:

Waju karrar bujilba jarramalinga. Warngku jambul bunday yundu nyajil jurrbu jirakal wangkar dakari. Yinyaymun jana stockman dungarida musteringkuda. Waybala kadan bamangka wajul baya buban jurilayku. Yala-yala June-July, jana dungayda manilda minya (12 December 1995, Mossman). - *Translated by Doreen Ball.*

Above: *Before and after fire.*

Charlie Denman

Charlie Denman was born and grew up on Green Hill Station, and from there moved to Cooktown and the Daintree Mission. Charlie's mother Lily was a *Yalanji* woman from *Buru*, and from her he gained a lot of knowledge of the yams, nuts, berries, fishing places, and hunting grounds of *Buru*. Charlie's mother was of the *Dabu* moiety, while his father, also Charlie, was *Wallar*. Charlie spent many years droving cattle from Laura Station, through *Buru*, and Daintree for the Mossman Butchering Company, and had extensive knowledge of the country and *bama* culture. Charlie married Eva, and together they had seven children, living and working around Eva's traditional country Daintree. They eventually moved to Mossman for better access to schools, and Charlie worked in the sugar cane industry. Charlie was highly respected in the Mossman district and always tried to help his own people. He explained *bama* fire management:

Burn the grass before the first storm come in, two days after you get all the young shoots coming up, that's the time stockmen go back, gotta go mustering.... before waybala came, bama light fires a bit earlier, around June/July, cause they gotta go and catch the minya (12 December 1995, Mossman).

Moja Harry Shipton
(Photo R.Hill)

Yarri-Kalbay

Yarri-Kalbay balkajin Kunanga, nyulu bundan yinyay bama-bamanji nyungunji ngamunji Claranji nganjananji Mojonji. Juku jabarrku janjanan yinyaykudabi nyungu bayan janjanan. Bama-bama jurrkijin Kankarr wawu yinymun. Yarri-Kalbay workmanijin-manijinya tin maninya Kunanga, Madjanga, Burungu yalarrku bubungu yindu-yindumbu. Yarri-Kalbayangku wunan Ena, Jalunji jalbu, bula yinyamun jurrkijin Banabila, bulanga sevenbala kangkal-kangkal. Yarri-Kalbay binal bajaku nyunguwunku Kukuku Nyungkulku yalarrku Jalunjimunku kukuku. Yarri-Kalbay jawun-karra wubul warrmbabungan, yalarrku janangan mungka kalbay- kalkay bundanarin Mangkalba, nyulu Yarri-Kalbayngka wundil-wundinya dingkibu jalundurr. Yarri-Kalbay kuku yirrkan-yirrkanya bubuku Yalanji-warrangda, North Queensland Land Councilangka 1970s, yinyamun nyulu work-manya baja Cape York Land Councilanda yalarrku Yalanjinji bamawunku bubuku 1990s. Yarri-Kalbay yalarrku kuku wambal-wambanya nyunguwunbu jawun-karranda nyulu majaman, yalarrku workman Community Rangernji yinyamun Elders Justice Groupmunji. Buyunkay nyulu wulanda nyulu kari nyajin nyungu bijarrmun bayan ngaranya yinyaykuna jabarrba jukunukunya Kunanga. Yarri-Kalbayngka manu-bajabuku kuku balkal baya muyaraji:

Murara, yundu kariku waju balu muyar kunbay, muyar karida yundu wajuda, kunka wurar yaykarrmal- baja yinyayngka junjuy-junjuy wajujikuda… baya, yundu kujingarr, nganjin kariku wajul jikan, muyara (26 November 1996, Little Forks). - Translated by Lily Yougie

Harry Shipton

Harry Shipton was born at *Kuna*, Shipton's Flat, and lived there with all the *bama* and his parents, Mojo and Clara. A *jabarr* tree marks the site of his original house. Most of the bama were moved to Cooktown after the war. Harry worked in tin mining at Shipton's Flat, Main Camp, China Camp and other places. After Harry married Ena, a *Jalunji* woman, they moved to Bloomfield, and brought up their seven children. Harry had great depth of knowledge from both the *Kuku-Nyungkul* and *Jalunji* sides. He made many friends, including the hippies living at Cedar Bay, taking them along the coast in his boat. Harry championed *Yalanji* land rights, helping establish the first North Queensland Land Council in the 1970s, and working with the Cape York Land Council and the *Yalanji* native title claim in the 1990s. Harry contributed his knowledge to his people, serving on the Council, working as a Community Ranger and in the Elders Justice Group. Sadly, he passed away before he could achieve his dream of building his house once again under the *jabarr* tree at *Kuna*. Harry explained the importance of wind with fire:

Wind, you gotta stop until wind die down, no wind, you can burn....if the wind just blow up, it'll burn everywhere.... fire, you got to wait, we don't burn the grass now, when it's windy (26 November 1996, Little Forks).

Top Left: *Ena and Harry Shipton, Cedar Bay beach (Mangkalba). (Photo: R. Hill)*

Top Right *Open forest on the ridges and rainforest valleys, Shipton's Flat. (Photo: R. Hill)*

Jina-Babaji

Jimmy Johnson

(Photo R.Hill)

Jina-babaji

Jina-baji balkajin naka Myall Creek jarra badamunda Kulkinga bamananda buralba, nyulu maja Jalunku. Jina-bajinga ngamu Lena nganjan Naku, bulangan dajalkira Rene Jinabaji birubaynjida dingkinji wundinya Kulkimu schoolku Bloomfield bula karrkay bulalku. Jina-bajingka school bawan dingkijida dungan bubungu Lockhart, nyulu jalbu wunan burri Georigina. Bulanga sixbala kangkal-kangkal. Jina-baji ngadibajaku bubungu Cape York bundan, juku nyandal-nyandan yalarrku bulki muru bungal-bungan. Nyulu kadanbaja nyunguwunbu bubunguku bundanka Jajikalba nyulu kunban jiku. Jina-baji binalbajaku jilbaka, kuyuku, yalarrlu buralka Kulkika, Kawayka, Kabakarrngka, yalarrku juljalangka, buralka, yalarrku yirmbalka. Jina-bajingka balkal wanjarr. Yundu ngajingka nyungunin binalbungan jungkayku baya wajunku:

Nyulu wawu kari jikan wajunjinku, nganjin yinya jikan mujan warrbi ngaranka ngana balnji kaday yaluy (13 November 1995, Collins Creek). *- Translated by Kathleen Walker.*

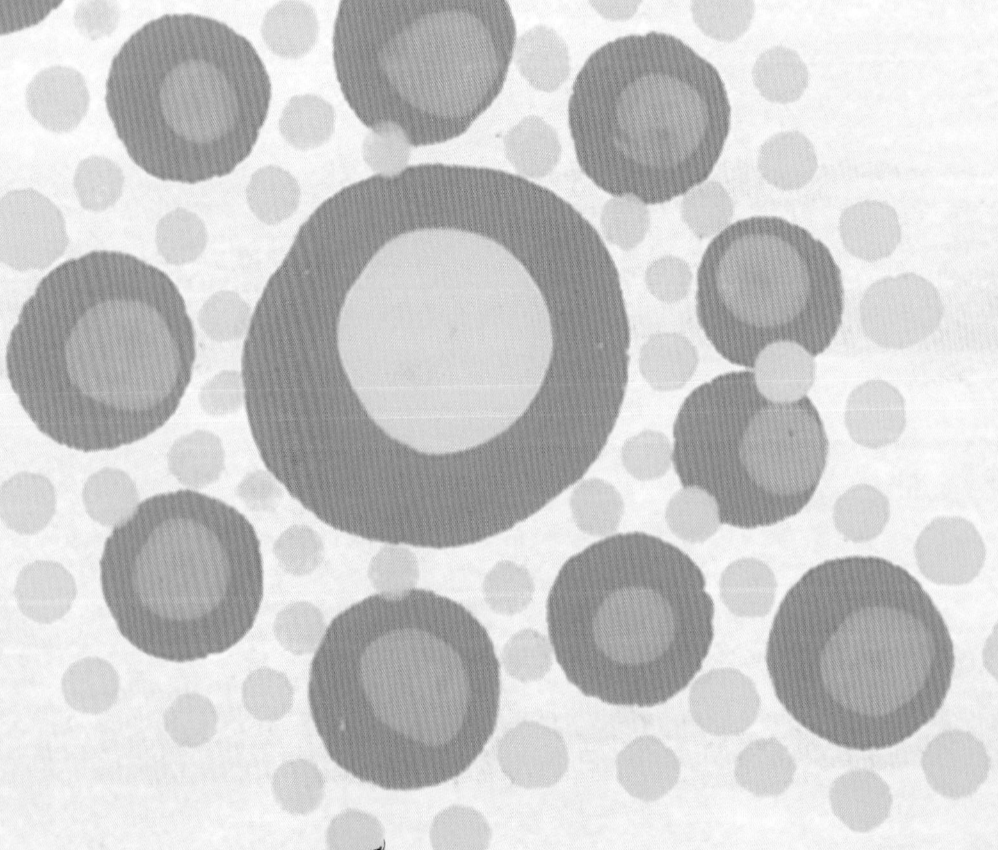

Jimmy Johnson

Jimmy Johnson was born near the mouth of Myall Creek just south of Cape Tribulation in a large *bama* camp, and was a *Jalunji* traditional owner. Jimmy's parents, John and Lena, rowed he and his sister Rene by boat from Cape Tribulation to school in Bloomfield each week when they were young. Jimmy left school to travel on a boat to Lockhart, where he married Georgina. They had six children. Jimmy lived on Cape York for many years, working in timber cutting and mustering. He returned to his traditional country and lived at Bloomfield in his last years. Jimmy had extensive skills in hunting and fishing, and knowledge of the coastal estates along Cape Tribulation, *Kaway*, and Cow Bay, including the location of burials, old camps and story places. Jimmy explained how his grandfather taught him to be careful with fire:

He don't want the grass to be burnt because we need that grass to make humpies when we come here to camp (13 November 1995, Collins Creek).

Top Left: *Jack Solomon, Jimmy's grandfather, was a Solomon Islander brought to Australia for cane cutting. He lived at Bailey's Creek until he died late in 1939. (Photo courtesy of the Mason family).*

Top Right: *Cape Tribulation (Kulki).*

Dolly Youngie
(Photo R.Hill)

Ngalba-yalbay

Ngalba-Yalbay dindarrmun kankal bulanga Bawanyanga, Jina-kurru-kurrumu. Nyulu balkajin Julaymba. Nyulu maralku dunganya Julaymba Wujal Wujal dungan dunganya dingkiji birungubayji manil-maninya juru kala kalbayku nyunguwunji babarranji Yimaranji. Nyulu wunan Waljinga Yougie bundan Dikarrba. Nyunu Ngalba-yalbayngu elevenbala kankal-kankal, nyulu yalarrku nyungu jinkurr Bakakiri, yabaju Dukuldandi bulangan jirray bungan jananga ngamu/nganjan wulan. Ngalba-yalbay nyulu jakalbamun ngujakuranmun kukungu nyunguwunbu milkajanay/ nyujakuramun, balji wukurril-wukurrinya, marra, wukay damal-damanya. Nyulu yalarrku jalbu-jalbu kulngkul-kulngkul kujil-kujinya. Ngalba-yalbay dunganya wunganya balnji Nganjin Naka-Nakamun Yalanji-warra bubungu, nakamun Kaba-Kadamun dungan Mangkalba kadanbaja Dikarrba, dakanbaja madjanga wangkar Kijanga. Nyulu Ngalba-yalbay binal bajaku ngujakuramunku:

Ngadi-ngadiku ngujakuraku junkurrji-bajaku. Nyungu, kuku,bijarr, yundu wungka badi, kadan ngujakuramun jakalbamun (31 October 1996, Thompson Creek translated from Yalanji by Adelaide Baird). *- Translated by Eileen Walker*

Dolly Yougie

Dolly was the fourth child of Nellie Yerry and Paddy Schuan. She was born at the Daintree River, and spent her youth between the Daintree River and Bloomfield, once rowing a boat all the way with her sister Elsie. She married Youngaman Yougie and settled at Thompson Creek. Dolly gave birth to eleven children and became foster mother to several of her own sisters and brothers when her parents passed away. Dolly was highly respected for her depth of knowledge of *Yalanji* culture, of the *Ngujakura*, of making dilly bags, processing *marra* and *wukay*, and the skills of mid-wifery. Dolly also walked over and camped on much of the Eastern *Yalanji* country, from Bailey's Creek to Cedar Bay, from *Dikarrba* to Main Camp and Roaring Meg. Dolly reflected on *bama* law:

The power was strong in the old days, in those days. You got a story, that's your dreaming, to sing.... that comes from the Ngujakura, from the beginning of time (31 October 1996, Thompson Creek translated from *Yalanji* by Adelaide Baird).

Top Right: *Detail of a dilly bag (balji) made from Black Palm fibre.*

Middle Right: *Eileen Walker and Dolly Yougie on the banks of Thompson Creek (Dikarrba). (Photo: R. Hill)*

Below Right: *There are strong cultural restrictions on who can go to this and other mountains in Yalanji country.*

Dukul - Dandi

Bobby Yerry
(Photo S.Coates)

Dukul-dandi

Dukul-dandi balkajin Lundin, karrkaymunku nyulu yaluy Dikarrbaku bundandan, nyulu yaluy schoolbu walan. Warruku Dukul-dandi workmanijin stationba yalarrku yaluy bada sawmillba. Yinyamun Lutheran missionaries kadan 1960s bubu kidan Wujal Wujal. Dukul-dandi majaman nyungununku jawun-karranga. Nyulu mara dajin bayan, junjuy-junjuy janaymaninka bana, sewerage, power. Dukul-dandi nyungun jawun-karranka maja-bungan, 10yearsmunku nyulu kujin. Dukul-dandi bula waybala Chris Anderson jawun-jawunman, nyulu Chris anthropologist manun-manunman Dukul-Dandinka nyunguwunku ngujakuramunku. Dukul-dandingka milbil-milbinya bubu yirmbal Wujal Wujal baralkuda yijarrin. Yinyamun jarra nyiku-nyiku nyulu kuku dajin junkayku Elders Justice Groupanda yalarrku native title claimanda. Dukul-dandinka balkan wanjarr bamanga ngalku ngujakuramun:

Bamangka nyunguku kuku wukurril, bamangkaku bubu kujil, bamangka bubu kujil-kujin ngadimunku, bamangka jimalku ngurrbal-ngurrbalnya bayaka ngadi-ngadiku, bamangka ngalku yaralbakunya wajul ngalku kari walal madjanga (30 April 1996, ZigZag).

- Translated by Francis Walker

Bobby Yerry

Bobby was born at Thompson Creek and spent his early years in the Bloomfield valley, where he attended school. As a young man, Bobby worked as a station hand and at the local sawmill. When the Lutheran mission established at Wujal Wujal in the early 1960s, Bobby became the major contact person. He helped build the mission dwellings, and establish water, sewerage and power. Bobby was the first *Bama* Chairman elected by his people and held the position for ten years. Bobby had a close friendship with Chris Anderson, an anthropologist who respected Bobby's extensive cultural knowledge. Bobby helped identify and protect sacred sites during the construction of the Bloomfield Road. In later years Bobby placed his wisdom and guidance behind community issues like the Elders Justice Group and the native title claim. Bobby explains *bama* fire Law:

Bama carry his own Law, bama look after the land, bama been looking after the land for years and years, bama been using fire stick.... early days, country much better, bama burn cool time, fire don't go right into that scrub (30 April 1996, Zig Zag).

Top Left: *(L-R) Bramston Dick on horse, Matthew Friday, Johnny Bassani and Gregory Dick with back turned at the horse stables in Wujal Wujal community.*

Top Right: *Bobby Yerry with anthropologist Chris Anderson. (Photo: S. Coates)*

Wambi

Jack Pierce

Wambi

Wambi nyulu balkajin jirrayman Gungarade, jurrkijin baja Julaymba warruku. Nyungu ngamu Yalanji jalbu Burumun. Wambinka Thelma wunan nyulu Yalanji maja bubuku Julayngka, bulanga kangkal-kangkal six bala. Wambi ngadi bajaku bulki wundil-wundin Lauramun, naka Julaymba bada Kubidi warngkar Mareeba. Wawu yinyamun nyulu bundaynda Kubidikuda bungku-jabangakuda nyandal-nyandanjinya, bungkujaba kunban yinya buyun-bajaku work. Wambi binal bajaku, nyulu yalarrku mala work, nyulu kuku yirrkan yalarrku mara dajinya junjuy-junjuy janay maninka nyunguwunbu jawun-karranga. Burrangka nyungun mara wajun nganjan Wambimu, junkurr janan ngalmbundu jana balu nyungun Wambi yunganka Palm Island.

Bama, jana jilba dungay jananga mayi nubinka. Jana baya wajul karirrku yalbay jarra buban wajul, jananka julmbanunku, kadaranka jurrbungu nukan-nukanjinka, Jana dungan baya wajul jilbaka.... Wungarijimalda kari baya wajulbaja (16 April 1996, Mossman).

- Translated by group - Doreen Ball, Eileen Walker, Francis Walker, Kathleen Walker and Lily Yougie

Above: *Wallabies come and feed on new grass following fires.*

Jack Pierce

Jack Pierce was born and grew up in Cooktown, moving to Daintree as a young man. His mother was a *Yalanji* woman from *Buru*. Jack married Thelma, a *Yalanji* traditional owner from Daintree, and together they brought up six children. Jack spent many years droving cattle from Laura, through Daintree to Mossman and Mareeba. After marrying, he settled down to cane cutting and lived in Mossman. In the off season he would work contract-felling scrub by axe, very hard work. Jack was highly respected as a hard worker and a strong contributor to helping the development of *bama* people's interests. Jack's step father, Charlie Denman, stood up to the police when they tried to take Jack to Palm Island.

Aboriginal, they've got to go and hunt for their food. They light fires, don't light all the bush, light a little bit, enough to keep them going, all the kangaroo and wallaby come and feed there on the green grass, they go and light a place just to hunt on.... when it gets to the real hot time, they won't light no more then (16 April 1996, Mossman).

Alec Olbar
(Photo R.Hill)

Babaji

Babaji kankal bulanga Wudakaringa Kulkamu balkajin Kulkinga. Babaji junkurrji Jalunji buwumbuku binal bajaku jalunku, mayika, minyaka, dingkiji dungan-dungaynya badurji. Nyulu dingkinga workmalman, dakal-dakalba janjil-janjilnya jalundurr Townsvillemun yarra wangkar Torres Straitsnga kuwa-kuwa Gulfburr. Nyulu wunan Emily bula Banabila bundaydanda, bula yalarrku bundan Banabila, Jajikal. Babaji bula Emilyinya kangkal-kangkal six bala. Bula jurrkijin wangkarkuda Missionbada, bundandan, nyulu Babaji workman bayanda ngaral-ngaran, bananka junjuy-junjuy yijarril-yijarrin yalarrku bayan kanbal janaymalil-malin. Yinyamun ngadi-ngadimunku, Babajingka kuku wambajinya nyunguwunku bubuku. Bubuku kuku junkurrji yirrkanka. Babajingka balkan wanjarr bura baya wajul jilbaka:

Bama murumal bayaburr ngaluri kujinka yinyamun ngaluri nyunil birrabu, kaki ngaluri dakalbaja jana nyunil baja, kaki minya bikibiki, kadar wandiri jana kunilkuda. Ngana ngalku wajuda madja bunjalku kujinka. (28 May 1996, Weary Bay).

- Translated by group - Doreen Ball, Eileen Walker, Francis Walker, Kathleen Walker and Lily Yougie

Alec Olbar

Alec Olbar, *Babaji*, the son of Oscar and Topsy, was born at Cape Tribulation. Alec was a strong *Jalunji* man with great knowledge of the sea, of traditional maritime culture, most at home on a boat, fishing. He spent a lot of his life working on boats, diving for pearl shell between Townsville and the Torres Straits, and around to the Gulf. He settled in the Bloomfield Valley after marrying Emily, living at *Banabila*, Weary Bay and Bottom Camp. Alec and Emily had six children. They moved to the Mission for some years where Alec worked in carpentry and plumbing, helping establish the buildings and infrastructure. In later years Alec contributed his extensive knowledge of language, culture and stories, to the fight for recognition of land and cultural rights. Alec explains enclosed hunting fires:

The bama get around, and they block off, keep the fire inside the line, they put the fire out with the leaf, fire will stay in, any fire comes out they put it out, then anything that come out they catch, wallabies, pigs.... we should burn it now, stop the rainforest coming in, keep it open (28 May 1996, Weary Bay).

Above Left: *Alec Olbar standing in open forest patch at Cedar Bay (Mangkalba). (Photo: R. Hill)*

Above Centre: *Adelaide Baird, Emily Olbar and Phillip Olbar at Cedar Bay (Mangkalba). (Photo: R. Hill)*

Above Right *Alec Olbar in front of a cycad (marra). (Photo: R. Hill)*

Ngadijina
Wilma Walker
(Photo R.Hill)

Ngadijina

Ngadijina, kankal jalbu bulanga Jack Carolanga Jessie Buchananga, wurunbu Jinkalmu nyuluku balkajin Mossman wawubajanga, nyulu yalbayman bundanday nyunuwunji jawun-karranji. Ngadijina kamingka nyungun ngakin baljinga, ngalmbu kadarin yarrka-yarrka waki-waki wundijinka. Ngadijina marri jakalbamun jalbu bubuku Kubidimunku, nyulu marri jalbu milka janay nyungundu nyulu binal bajaku ngujakuraka. Ngadijina jurrkijin Julaymba, Jangkiba wunan, bulanga ninebala kankal-kankal. Bula workmanjin junkurr muruku Julaymba Missionba, bulanga bayan ngaral-ngaran yalarrku mara dajil-dajin jawun-karranga. Bula Ngadijina Jangkibangka kaban exemption Governmentdamun manin Bamanga Act in 1961 jurrkijinka Mossman. Ngadijina mala balji. Nyulu binalbal TAFE, university yalarrku yarrka-yarrka schoolba, nyungu junjuy-junjuy nyulu balkan yijayirrin Sydney museum. Ngadijina wuljaljiku kuku yirrkan-yirrkay nyunguwunku Yalanjinka bubuku kukuku. Nyulu balkan wanjarr baya wajunya yunu dungu yinyada yunun wawurr-wawurrbungan maralku.

Jana baya wujun, kamba-kamba binga-binga jana wulngku badin, jana bayanga janarin, yinyamun bayabu kububu warra wajun. Jana yalaman "Yundu yalbaymal kari dunyu yindu mana, Yundu yanyuku wawurr kujida", jana kamba-kamba binga-binga kuku yirrkay baja kunbayda (16 October 1995, Mossman).

- Translated by group - Doreen Ball, Eileen Walker, Francis Walker, Kathleen Walker and Lily Yougie

Wilma Walker

Above Left: *Wilma weaving a dilly bag (balji). (Photo: R. Hill)*

Above Right: *Wilma's grandmother hid her in a dilly bag (balji) when the policemen came to take the half-caste children.*

Wilma, *Ngadijina*, the daughter of Jack Carol and Jessie Buchanan, was born in a *wurun* at *Jinkalmu* on the Mossman River, and grew up living with all the *bama*. Wilma's grandmother hid her in a dilly bag, *balji*, when the policemen came to take the half-caste children. Wilma is a senior traditional owner for the Mossman area, and a respected elder with a depth and breadth of cultural knowledge. Wilma moved to Daintree when she married Norman, and together they raised nine children. They worked very hard at the Daintree Mission, building their own house and helping other families. Wilma and Norman gained their exemption from government control under the Aboriginal Act in 1961 and moved to Mossman. Wilma is an expert at weaving *balji* in the traditional *Yalanji* style. She teaches TAFE, University and school students, and has exhibits in the Sydney Museum. Wilma is still fighting for recognition of *Yalanji* cultural rights and knowledge. She explains how a fire was used for a promise ceremony with her future husband in her youth:

They make a fire, all the old people sing, dance around, and they stand around the fire, and they get that fire and put it through your body like that, and say, when you grow up you don't get another dunyu, you wait for this boy, they talk, talk in language all over, all over (16 October 1995, Mossman).

Alma Kerry
(Photo R.Hill)

Binda Buyun

Binda Buyun kankal jalbu bulanga Baybunga Milidamu, balkajin Burungu. Nyulu yalbayman jilba dungan-dunganya mayiburr minyaburr nubin-nubijinya nyungu-wunbu bubungu Bulban, Kankaji, Mangkalba, Ngalbanga. Wawu yinyamun nyulu wunan Jalunji dingkar burri Burringanjan, Binda Buyun bundandaynda Banabila nyunguwunji kankalji Abinji. Binda Buyungku balji balkanya mawumun ngakumun, yalarrku, oil balkanya jirimandimun. Nyulu binal bajaku bubuku yirmbalka bijarril-bijarrilnya jalunji minya mujal-mujanka. Nyulu kuku bamaku balkan-balkawanya. Nyulu balkan nyungu kuku ngujakuramunku.

Nganjin dunganya marrakanji Ngalbanga, Mangkalba, marrakan warrbibu nyandan birubay balkanya. Nganjin jilba dunganya duliburr nubi-nubijinya marranga walmbaburr minyaka baja-bajaka, kulnguku, binanjalba.Ngalbanga, ngadi-ngadiku bubu bunjal nyiku-nyiku madjabu kanbinkuda, nganjin wukay kari manil baja jukarmun (13 November 1995, Wujal Wujal, translated from Yalanji by Adelaide Baird).

- Translated by group - Doreen Ball, Eileen Walker, Francis Walker, Kathleen Walker and Lily Yougie

Alma Kerry

Above Left: *Looking over Cowie.*

(Photo: R. Hill)

Above Right: *Robert Baird and Alma Kerry.*

(Photo: R. Hill)

Alma Kerry, the daughter of John and Melita Baird, was born at *Buru*. She grew up with the bama life, hunting, gathering and walking over her country to *Bulban, Kankiji,* Cedar Bay and Cowie. After marrying Jimmy Kerry, a *Jalunji* man, Alma settled at *Banabila* and devoted her life to caring for their daughter Alice. Alma crafted dilly bags from *mawu* and *ngakan*, and made traditional Yalanji *items* like coconut oil. She knew all the story places, and dreaming tracks along the *Jalunji* side, and loved to spend her days collecting shellfish and fishing on the reefs and beaches. Alma was a magnetic story-teller who spoke only *Kuku-Yalanji* language. She described her life in the early days:

We used to just go by canoe to Cowie, Cedar Bay, canoe made with a stone axe to shape it, paddle. We used to go hunting in the burnt areas, looking around, in a hollow log, for bandicoot, blue tongue lizard and frilly lizard. At Cowie, it used to be open, now it's grown back really thick, we can't get wukay on the beachfront there any more because of the rainforest (13 November 1995, Wujal Wujal, translated from Yalanji by Adelaide Baird).

Ngadiku, Ngujakura - Ngalku

Ngadiku ngujakuraku, ngananga bijarr junkurrjiku, ngananga jawun-karrangka bubu balkan, jana ngujakura bawan. Kanbalda marri-marringka yinyarrin kuku junkurrji balkanka ngalkuku kabanba.

Challa/Jinkarr balkan wanjarr baya wajul, jana nyurrbal jimal durral jukumun:

Jimal, yinya baya juku. Yinyakudabi jakalbamun jimal, Yunu burri Jimalili, Yinyamunkuda ngaluri dakan. Jimalili madjanga, nyulu junbirrmanda, walu nyulkurrijin junbirr. Nyungu jurru jalngkun, nyulu baya baka, nyungu dakal buban, juku durral nyurrbal-nyurrbanya (4th December 1995, Collin's Flat)

- Translated by Lily Yougie

Charlie Denmanangka balkal wangjarr jurrbu dakalbaja wawu ngalkumun. Yinya nganangaku ngujakuramun:

Yala-yala ngawa Kija bujil janjil-janjin Dumubajanga nyulu Kija yirrkan-yirrakajin bama kari kadarin ngayurrku yirrkan-yirrkajin. Jikanangka karrban karrkay bamangka kari nyugun manin banamun. Ngalku yalbay wajul jikan jurrbu dakalbaja. Yinya jikan jirakal dakal bijarr kuku bamandamun (12 December 1995, Mossman).

- Translated by Doreen Ball

Left: *Morning light on Bloomfield Falls.*

In the beginning: the Ngujakura and Ngalku

In the *Ngujakura*, the dreaming which is also still now, ancestral beings made the country, and left stories which defined Aboriginal Law/Lore. Some elders have chosen to share some important fire stories for this book.

Peter Fischer explains how fire was first made by twirling *jimal* sticks from the *durral* tree:

Jimal, that's the fire stick. The first one that made that jimal fire, his name was jimalili, that's what the flames started from. Jimalili is in the scrub, he is a lizard now, a very nice looking animal. He's got a very sharp elbow, jurru jalngkun, because he's so much on making fire, he has long skinny arms from rubbing the durral sticks together (4 December 1995, Collin's Flat).

Charlie Denman describes how new grass shoots up after burning because of the actions of ancestral beings in the *Ngujakura*:

When that little baby, Kija the moon, was drowning in the Roaring Meg now. Singing out for help. Nobody came, nobody help him, singing out. That grass grab hold of that little fellow, he got saved, even though the bama couldn't help him. Only that grass could save him, Kija. Anyone burn that grass now, it doesn't matter how big a bush fire, the young shoots come up. See the green shoots coming up, that's the dreamtime story from the bama (12 December 1995, Mossman).

Top Left: *A boy paints a snake on rock beside the Bloomfield River.*

Middle Right: *Dawn on the Bloomfield River.*

Below Right: *The jimal plant is used to make firesticks. (Photo: R. Hill)*

Above: *Mangrove forest.*

Binda Buyungku kuku balkal wanjarr Dabu, madjaka mawal bula Walarr ngalkalji bayaka kuniwan:

Ngujakuraku ngadiku Burungu, Kijanka jirrakan ngalku baya. Dabu jananga mawal karrkay, wunbar madjaji. Dabungku wawu kari nyajinka baya wumbulbajaku jana yinilman kadan jina wajujinji. Dabu yirrkan-yirrkankuda baya ngalku kari yarrku waju. Yamba baya ngalku kari kunban. Nyulu warrin baya ngalkumun, nyulu warrinkuda mankurrumunbu jalaman. Yinya yirmbalda nyulu Dabu dungan bama kari dungay mankurrumbu yulbaka, mayi minya kari nuka yinyamun bubumun kari dungay jilba yinyay (13th November1995,Wujal Wujal). - *Translated by Eileen Walker*

Binda Buyunwungku balkal wanjarr Jibul bula Kalbu bural kidan ngalkalba nyiku yinyakubi:

Jibulanka jikan kalka yilbal-yilban yiyanmun. Nyuluku nyunguku minya daman. Kalbu, dikal, kunin-kuniwan. Jibulangka minya nukal-nukan, nyulu nyuluku ngandal yakajin kuyanda. Murrka yinyaku bawajinda. Bula kalbu/Jibul kariku kuni-kuniwanku. Yinyamun Jibulanka baya wajun, minyaka. Yamba bulanga kuli kari kunban. Yinya bubu bunjalda bural bayamun. Bula yinyaykuda baya wajun (29 November 1995, Wujal Wujal). - *Translated by Kathleen Walker*

Above: *Adelaide Baird extinguishing an inappropriate fire with green branches at China Camp (Buru). (Photo: R. Hill)*

Alma Kerry describes how *Dabu*, the rainforest honey bee, and *Walarr*, the open forest bee, fought over fire.

In the beginning, at Buru, Kija the moon had started a fire. Dabu are those little bees that make wild honey in the rainforest. Dabu didn't want the fire to spread out. That fire was too hot, they were frightened Kadar the wallaby would burn his feet. Dabu cut some branches and leaves to put out the fire, by beating on it. Dabu was singing out "don't make too much fire". But the fire didn't stop. So he ran away from the fire, he flew away and ended up near the mangroves down there. There's yirmbal, a spirit now, at the place where Dabu went. No-one can go near it or touch it. You're not to go near the mangroves, or eat anything from that area, shell, mussel, or walk around there (13 November 1995, Wujal Wujal, translated from *Yalanji* by Adelaide Baird).

Alma explains how *Jibul* and *Kalbu* created a big open forest patch, still there today:

Jibul the bat was throwing spears from there, using grass for spears. He speared himself some minya. Kalbu, a bird from the rainforest, was fighting with Jibul. They were fighting over minya. Jibul was eating the minya, and he cut himself in the mouth with a stone knife. The mark is still there today. Kalbu and Jibul kept fighting and fighting. Finally Jibul made a fire, to cook the minya. They were still fighting each other. That's why the area is baldy now, that's where they made the fire (29 November 1995, Wujal Wujal, translated from *Yalanji* by Adelaide Baird).

Karen Gibson, Dilbal, yanyu ngurma julkan kukumun nyunguwundumun ngajinandamun Kwinyalangka balkan ngalkuku:

Ngadiku Yalanji-warra bama jilba dungarinya. Jana kadan-baja jilbamun, jananga baya yalu-kunban. Jana jinkalmu yungan jukungu dakanka walu wukurrinka baya, yamba nyulu jurrlilman, yalaman nyulu kari nyajin. Yinyamun jana Bajalji yungan jukungu dakanka, bayanka nubijinka, yamba nyulu yalarrku jurrilman. Yinyamun baja-baja jana yungan jukungu dakanka walu wukurrinka yalaman, yamba nyulu nyajin ngarrbalda baya ngakin. Jana Yalanji-warra bama dungan jananga baya maninka baja bama ngarrbalandamun. Yamba nyulu Kijangka balar yalbay kunjan, bubu ngarrbal ngandanyarrkuda. Jana bama ngarrbal-ngarrbal kuyuman, ngawingaman, yala kanbal junjuy-junjuy jalunji milbin yanyu bada-bada julkan ngurmanga. Yinyanka nganjin Yalanji-warranka bamangka janangan manil-manil nukanka nyiku.

-Translated by Francis Walker.

Karen Gibson, *Dilbal*, painted this fire story from her grandfather, George Kulka:

One day all the Yalanji bama went out hunting. When they came back they discovered their fire was missing. They sent the brown snake up a tree to look for the fire, but he lied to them and told them he couldn't see it. They sent the taipan up a tree to look for the fire, but he lied to them too and told them he couldn't see it. Then they sent the blue-tongued lizard up a tree to look out for the fire, and he told them he could see another tribe had taken their fire. The Yalanji bama went to get their fire back from the other tribe. But Kija, the moon, called up a big tide and the sea came and covered all the land where the other tribe was. The other tribe all turned into fish, turtle and other sea animals shown in the bottom of this painting. That's why the Yalanji bama hunt all those sea animal today.

The fire story painted by Karen Gibson shows why the Yalanji bama hunt sea creatures today.

Left: *Yalanji country from Mt. Sorrow.*

Above: *Bloomfield Falls.*

Below: *Fringing coral reefs near Cape Tribulation (Kulki).*

Wanja-Wanjaku Waybal-Waybal kadan:-

Yalanji-warrangka ngadi-ngadiku bubungu muruku bundarin.

Jinbaldaku jurrki manin waybalangaka jalunmun. Ngulunganjaku Captain Cook yala Captain Kingangka jajarrijin Kulkinga yala (Bloomfield) 1819/21; yala bijilima station yinyay jajarrijin Low Isles, Hope Islandmun Annan wawubajanga yala yala 1860s 70s. Bubu walu wukurrin nyungunji Hana-anji 1872. Ngulunganjaku mungari nyandan kadan jalunmun yala Mossmanum, Julaymun, Bloomfieldmun 1874 juma wukurrin bungku-jaba farmersangka.

Wubul Kuku-Yalanji bama workmun ngulunganjaku bungku-jaba nandajin Bloomfield 1880s. Nganjin yalarrku workman bungkujabanga Mossman bulkinga Julaymba. Wubulbajaku miner's kadarin Burungu Kunanga kulji warrmbabungan nyulunganjaku 1880s, nganjin workman jananda ngulunajakunya, Yalanji dingkar, Romeomun warrmba bungan, kulji Kunanga murubuku waybalanji. Bubu jakalbaku balkan (Bloomfield) 1890s kunban 1900. Kulibaka ngadi-ngadiku mabarrda kunin-kuniwanya ngulunganjaku. Nganjin binal wanjabu Bama ngalmbungku marrkinda kunin bubungu nganjinanga jawun-karra. Nganjinnanga bamanga bubu. Wawu yinyamun majangka yalaman bamanga kujil-kujinka Act 1897, kanbal nganjinanga jawun-karra yungajin bubungu yinduymbu.

Ngayu balkal yunudu junjuy-junjuy ngadiku wanjarrmalman, Jana kunin bama yala wayilbala kaya yundu binal, buyunbajaku, Ngayu nyajin ngayku Jawun-karra dunganya mara cuffs munji. Jalbu jalbu yalarrku wubulku. Burumun yungajin Palm Island, Yarrabah (Peter Fischer, 5 December 1995, Wujal Wujal). *-Translated by Doreen Ball*

When the Waybala Came:

Yalanji Survival in the Contact Era

The dramatic changes of the *waybala* invasion began gradually, and from the sea. Firstly Captain Cook; then Captain King landed at Cape Tribulation and Bloomfield in 1819/21; and beche-de-mer stations were established at Low Isles, Hope Island and the Annan River mouth during the 1860s and 70s. Land exploration started with Hann in 1872. The first cedar cutters also came in from the sea, starting at Mossman, Daintree and Bloomfield all around 1874, and were soon followed by sugar cane farmers.

Above Left: *Kuku-Yalanji people at Roaring Meg Falls, circa 1884. (Source: Courtesy of John Oxley Library - #103571).*

Above Middle: *Kuku-Yalanji plantation workers near the Bloomfield River, 1883. (Source: Courtesy of John Oxley Library - #103570).*

Above Right: *Mossman cane farm, 1904. (Source: Courtesy of John Oxley Library - #143591).*

Many *Kuku-Yalanji* people worked for the first sugar plantation at Bloomfield in the 1880s. We also worked for sugar farmers in Mossman, and cattle farmers on the Daintree. Hundreds of miners arrived at *Buru* and *Kuna* (Shipton's Flat) when tin was discovered there in the early 1880s, and we worked for them from the very earliest times. A *Yalanji* man, Romeo, discovered the tin at *Kuna* together with a *waybala.* A mission was started at Bloomfield in the 1890s, but it closed by 1900. Violence was common in the early days. We know where the Native Police shot many of our people in camps. After the government declared the *Aboriginal Protection and Prohibition of the Sale of Opium Act* in 1897, some of our people were taken away:

I've got to tell you how things have been happening, they shootthe black like a wild dingo you know, so bad.... I seen my people go with the handcuffs, the women and all, in China Camp, taken away to Palm Island and Yarrabah (Peter Fischer, 5 December 1995, Wujal Wujal).

Workanya waybalanda farmunbu/miningbu nganjinan jurrkinji bubungu yinduymbu jurilayku 20th Century. Yalanji-warra bama bundan bubungu karangkalba miner'sanda, Burungu, Kunanga bungku-jabanga bubungu Brie-Brie, Junction wawubaja, karangkal-darrar Mossman wawubajaburr, jalundurr wangkar Kielynga wawubajanga, Yinyamun kadan-baja Kaba kada, Kulkinga, Bloomfield. Wilma Walker binalku wubulkuku bamawunku buralka Mossmanku:

***Above:** Kuku-Yalanji people at Banabila, 1884. (Source: Courtesy of John Oxley Library - #103565).*

Yundu nyajil wubulku bama, Jana dungay ngami-ngamiku wangkar wuburrdurr, Jana wulngku badi yala wawurr-wawurrmal (16 April 1996, Mossman).

Rene Sykes, mukul Jalunji jalbu junkurrji bajaku bubuku Kulkika, nyulu balkan nyungu ngujakuramun bubu. Wanjabu nyulu bundan nyulu karrkayku bundan wubulji Yalanji-warranji bamanji:

Nganjin wawu bajaku yinyayngka binga-binga, kamba-kamba yaluy. Yinyay jukara bundandan. Ngamu nganjan ngaji kami. Ngayu yaluy balkajin.... Ngayu wawu nyajinka ngayku kaminjarr karra jijakarra jalbumanya dingkarmanya yaluy. Kaki ngayu wulay nganya yarkin wundi-baja bubunguku Kulkinya nanda. Nganya ngayku wunbu ngamundmunbu nganjanandamunbu bulaku bundandan (13 November 1995, Cape Tribulation, Kulkinga).

- Translated by Doreen Ball

Above Left: *Kuku-Yalanji people at Bailey's Creek in the 1930s. (Source: Courtesy of the Mason Family).*

Above Right: *Kuku-Yalanji people at Daintree with A. Meston, 1896. (Source: Courtesy of John Oxley Library - #22150).*

However, working for *waybala* in farming and mining protected us from removals in the early part of the 20th century. *Yalanji* bama lived in big camps near the miners at China Camp and Shipton's Flat; on sugar farms at Brie-Brie, Junction Camp, and all along the Mossman River and coast; at Kiely Creek and other parts of the Daintree River; and all along the coast between Bailey's Creek, Cape Tribulation and Bloomfield. Wilma Walker remembers all the *bama* camps in the Mossman district:

You see all the bama, they go everywhere, on the hill, they sing out, singing out like this, happy way (16 April 1996, Mossman).

Rene Sykes, a senior *Jalanji* woman and strong traditional owner of Cape Tribulation, explains the importance of her traditional country, where she lived in her youth with hundreds of *Yalanji* people:

We used to love it here, old people here, along the beach there, sitting down, Mum, Dad and the grandparents, I was born here.... I'd like to see my grandchildren grow up here.... if I die, just bring me back, take me back to Cape Tribulation, and bury me, where my mother and father used to stay (13 November 1995, Cape Tribulation).

Above: *Sandra Burcombe, Warren Dickey and Linda Burchill take part in Naidoc week celebrations in Mossman.*

Ngadimunku buralbaku bubu juljal warrmba-bungan yubaku mukulbu bayanba:

Jana kari balkan-nyaku (bayan) Kulkinga . Jana ngaran bayan wurar juljalba yinyay (Eileen Walker, 30 October 1996, Thompson Creek, Dikarrba).

Nganjin workman nganjin, nganjinanga kulji kari manin- Yinyarrin kulji ngalmbundu dungarin, Wanyangka kulji dajil-dajin buban. Nganjin wuljaljiku balkan-balkaway maja-majanji kulji maninka baja:

Nganjin mara yijarrinya kabanba police Station sign-manya 12monthsmunku, a pound a week nganjin workmanya yaykarrku bulkimba, jamara, bungku-jaba nyandal-nyandanya, cow milkinbunganya. Yalayalaku nganjinangaku freedom, manin exemption kaban, nganjin binal workumku (Peter Fischer yala George Kulka, 19th June 1996, China Camp, Burungu).

- Translated by Doreen Ball

Above: *Rhoda McAllistair displays the breast plate of her grandfather, Wawooamittan, Mr. Diamond, a senior traditional owner of a clan estate on country that is now part of Mossman. (Photo: R. Hill)*

Important cultural sites and burial grounds are found near these old camps:

They shouldn't make that (houses) at the Cape, they're building those houses on top of our graves there (Eileen Walker, 31 October 1996, Thompson Creek).

Although we worked, we didn't get our money. That was all paid to the local police officer, who would occasionally give us a little. We are still fighting the government to get that money:

We used to put the thumb on the paper for the police station, sign on for 12 months, a pound a week.... we've been working very hard, cattle, scrub falling, cane cutting, running dairy cows.... that's when we got the first freedom, got the (exemption) ticket, all we ever knew was working (Peter Fischer and George Kulka, 19 June 1996, China Camp).

Above: *A traditional home (wurun) for the Kuku-Yalanji, within Mossman Gorge.*

Yala-Yala work buban kudamundu 1930's kanbal Yalanji bama jurrkimanin Missionba Julaymba/Kubidi. Maja-Majangaka kujil-kujinya wuljaljidaku, Nganjin babajinya marriedmanka, dunganka, workmanka. Nganjinanga kankal-kankal nganjinandamun dormitorynga mumban. Yinyamun bama nyubun-nyubunku jurrkil-jurrkinya janawunmun bubumun. Nganjin bama kanbal ngadibajaku workman yinya Missionba, bayan ngarajin, bana, sewerage, shops yijarrin:

Nganjin wawurr-wawurrku bundandarin nganjinanda-munbu bubungu. Ngayu binal ngayu yala-yala 12years oldku, yala-yala nganjinan jurrki-manin yinyamun. Nganya dormitorynga walay-manin. Nganjinanda balkan yurrangan jurrkilda wangkarda Wujal Wujalkuda missionbada (Lizzie Olbar, 28 May 1996, Jajikal).

Nyiku-nyiku nganjin nganjinku maja-majamal Kubidi/Wujal Wujalka nganjin balkan balkaway nganjinanka Native Title rightska. Bubuku ngujakuraka. - *Translated by Doreen Ball*

Top: *L-R, Clayton Baird, Brandon Christie, Trevor Yougie (Jnr.) and Leslie Schneider.*

Left: *Tamika Shipton.*

Right: *Yalanji children playing in the Bloomfield River,* **L-R,** *Ava Schneider, Talika Greenwool and Larissa Smith.*

There was less work after the 1930s depression, and more *Yalanji* people were forced to move to the missions established at Daintree and Mossman Gorge. The government controlled nearly every aspect of our life then. We had to get permission to marry, to travel, to work. Our children were separated from us in dormitories. The mission at Wujal Wujal started in the late 1950s, and people gradually moved there from the camps along the coast. Many of us worked very hard on these missions, building houses, water supplies, sewerage systems, and shops:

We were happy where we were living. I remember when I was twelve years old, when we got moved away from there. I got put in a dormitory. We were told to move out, further up to the mission (Lizzie Olbar, 28 May 1996, Jajikal).

Today we run our own lives and communities at Mossman and Wujal Wujal, but we are still fighting for proper recognition of our native title rights, our culture and our Law.

Buluriji/Wungariji, Ngalku wajukuda minyaka/ mayika

Yaluy bubungu Yalanjimunbu mayi jirraybajaku. Mayi wubul barka, yams, kuyu, kirbaji, bukiji, yulba, yangka, wunba - mayi wubul jiba wula-wula yaluy yamba yundu binalmanka wanjabu yala wanjarr nubinka. Nganjin Yalanji-warra binal wanyu mayikuda yala minyakuda yinyamun bubumun. Nganjin bubundu milka-janay wanyu nyulu balkal-balkal yala wanyu nyulu milbil-milbil nganjinanda.

Nganjinanga calendar yamba kari. Yamba nganjin Bamangka juku nyajil-nyajil. Yinya juku binalbajaku nganjin bama jarra yala. Yinyamun nganka jirakal dakal. Yinyanka balkal nganjinanda junjuy-junjuy mayi mayikuda (Peter Fischer, 14 November 1996, Buru).

Bamangka ngalku wajul yaralbakuna, June July, Bamangka nyajilkuda nganka mula-mula burri ngakun. Yinyamun bama jurrkijikada bubumun balaymun jarra-jarraku dakada jalungkarrka. Yundu yinya nyaka nyajil wawu-bajanga. Mayi wabal-wabal mula-mula. Bama jinbalku jurrkijikabaja wawubajamun (Bobby Yerry, 30 April 1996, Zig Zag homestead) - *Translated by Lily Yougie*

Top Left: *Flame tree (ngakun).*

Top Right: *Marra seeds after roasting over a fire.*

Seasons, Fire and Bush Tucker

Yalanji country is rich in wild food. Fruits, nuts, yams, fish, mammals, shell fish, insects - a delicious feast is here but you must know where and when to find it. Knowledge about seasons and bush tucker for Yalanji comes from the land. We listen to the country talk and watch the signs it give us *(Figure 1)*.

Top Left: *Edward Barney putting out fire.*

Top Right: *Roy Gibson watching fire.*

We don't have a calendar. Bama story goes by the tree. The tree knows better that we do. That's why the flower comes on. That tells us that's the time things are going to change (Peter Fischer, 14 November 1996, Buru).

Bama burn cool time, June or July, you see that red flower coming on the tree, ngakun. That's the time for shifting camp, moving out away from the floods country to the top of the hill. When you see that flower come along the river, and the walbul walbul cherry fruit is red, it's time to move back away from the river side (Bobby Yerry, 30 April 1996, Zig Zag homestead).

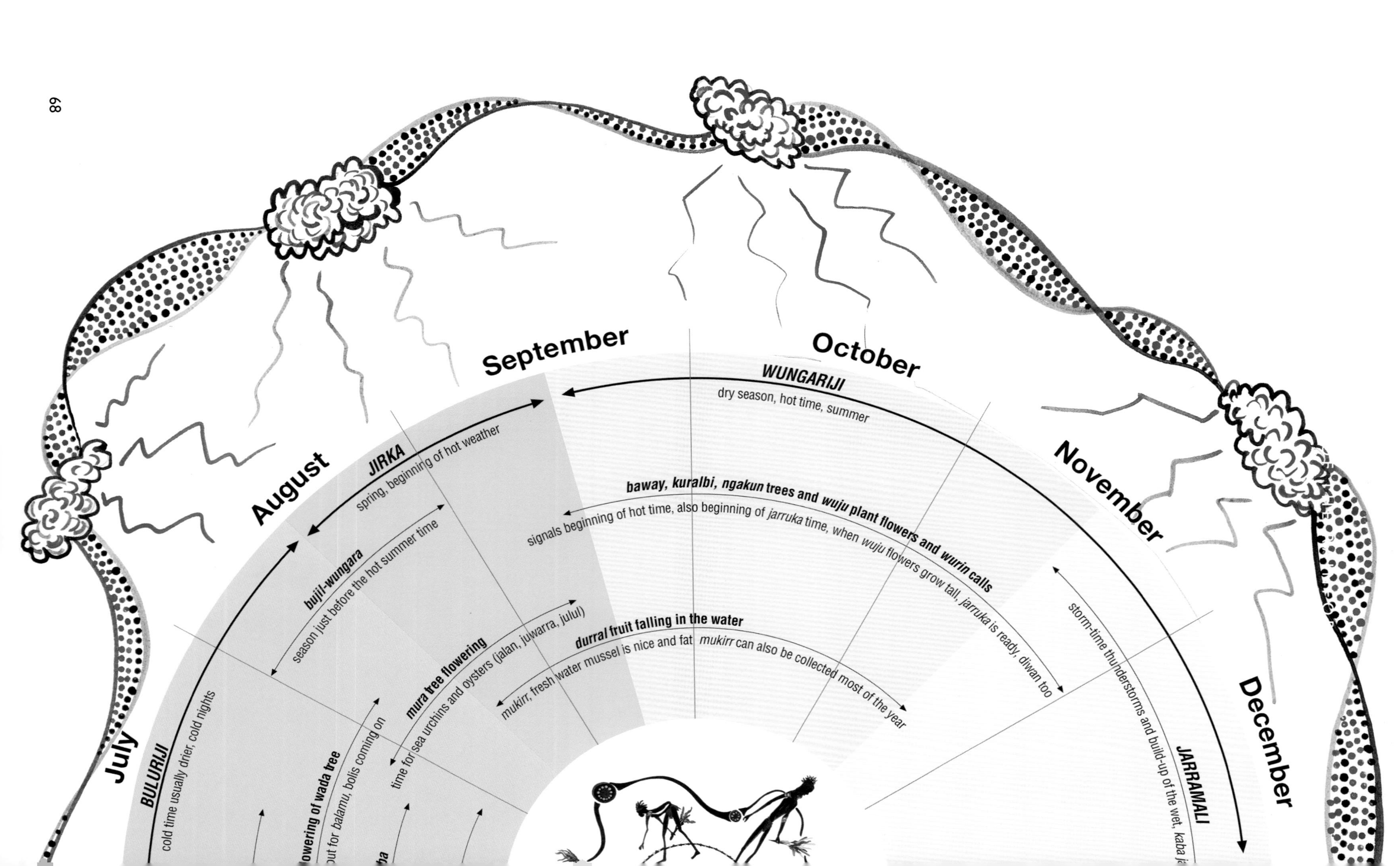

December
November
October
September
August
July
JARRAMALI
storm-time thunderstorms and build-up of the wet, kaba ja
WUNGARIJI
dry season, hot time, summer
baway, kuralbi, ngakun trees and wuju plant flowers and wurin calls
signals beginning of hot time, also beginning of jarruka time, when wuju flowers grow tall, jarruka is ready, diwan too
durral fruit falling in the water
mukirr, fresh water mussel is nice and fat mukirr can also be collected most of the year
JIRKA
spring, beginning of hot weather
bujiji-wungara
season just before the hot summer time
mura bee flowering
time for sea urchins and oysters (jalan, juwarra, juju)
owering of wada bee
ut for balamu, boils coming on
BULURIJI
cold time usually drier, cold nights

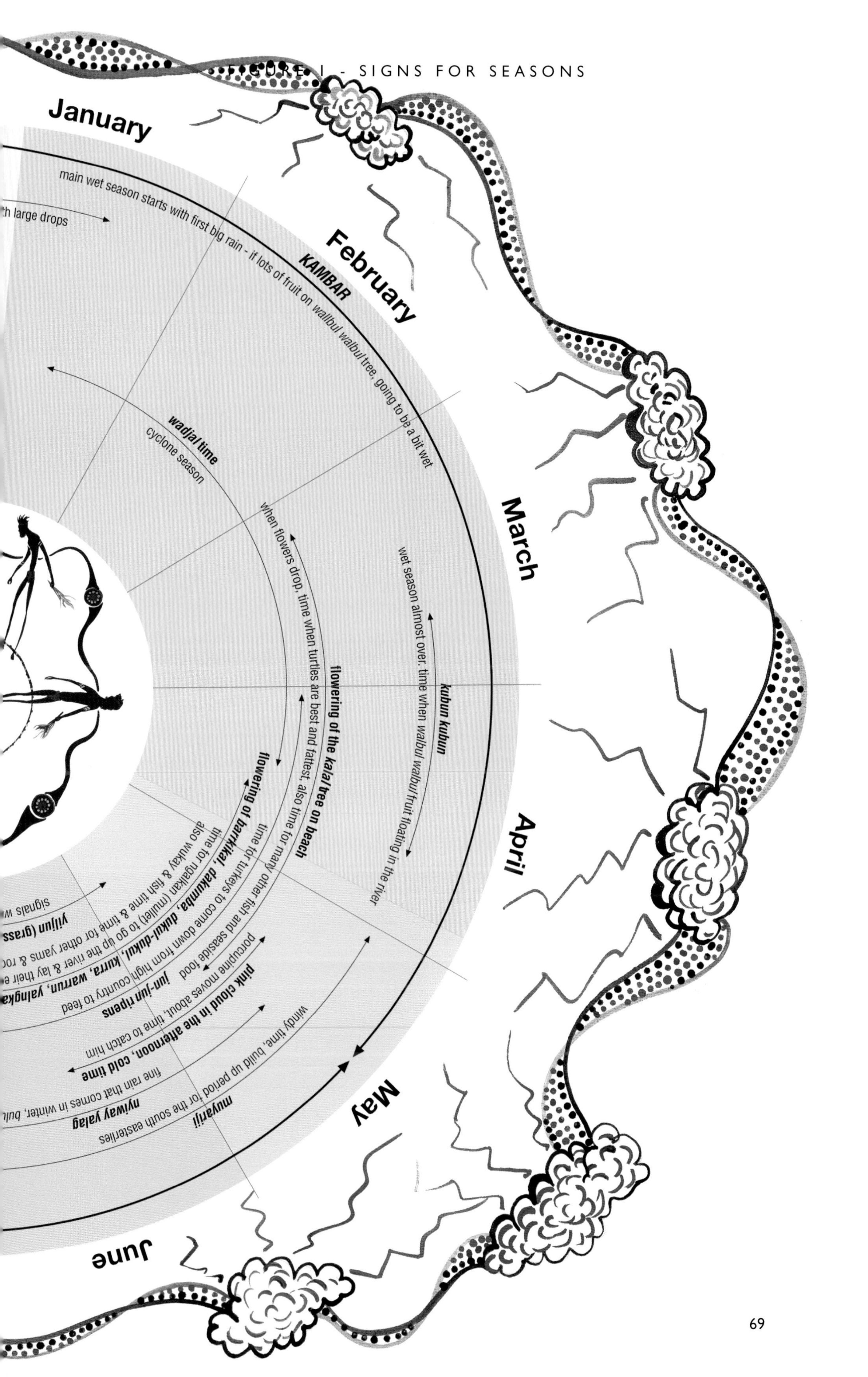

FIGURE 1 - SIGNS FOR SEASONS
January
February
March
April
May
June
large drops
main wet season starts with first big rain - if lots of fruit on walbul walbul tree, going to be a bit wet
KAMBAR
wadjal time
cyclone season
when flowers drop, time when turtles are best and fattest, also time for many other fish and seaside food
flowering of the kalal tree on beach
wet season almost over, time when walbul walbul fruit floating in the river
kubun kubun
flowering of barrkikal, dakumba, dukul-dukul, kurra, warrun,
time for turkeys to come down from high country to feed
time for ngalkan (mullet) to go up the river & lay their
also wukay & fish time & time for other yams &
jun-jun ripens
porcupine moves about, time to catch him
pink cloud in the afternoon, cold time
fine rain that comes in winter,
nyiway yalag
windy time, build up period for the south easterlies
muyarlil
yiljun
signals

Above: *Doreen Ball showing Yalanji girls how to look for wukay (yams).*

Madjaburr, ngalkaldarr, mangkurruburr/jukaraburr yala walngkaburr mayi yindu-yindu balkaji kija yindu-yindu *(Figure 2)*. Madja mayi jirray, nganjin mayi wubulbajaku walu yindu-yindu nukal marralmun bubumun. Kambara mayi madjanga jirray bajaku yala barka,bujabay, bijalambay. Kanbal madjaji mayi barka nganjin warrmba bungal bubumun dunanga. Ngadiku ngujakurangaku mayi marra dakal bujilba wungariji, warrmba bungal bunjalba ngalkalba. Yam dakal jukaranga karangkalba madjanga wukay mayi nyubunku, nganjinanga bamanga.

Jalundurr dulngkuburr jukarangka dajil minya walu-yindu -walu yindu *(Figure 3)*. Nganjin yalarrku minya kuyu ngawiya manil, Jalun marrkamal. Minya burngu jiba wula-wula bajaku, yamba nyiku-nyiku kari nyajilbaja. Ngalkalji minya yala kuyu kubarr, bayil, julaji, ngujay. Nganjin yalarrku kunil minya kadar, ngankin, kulngu, walkarr, yalarrku minya kaykay-kaykay. Minya diwan/jarruka diburr ngulkurr bajaku.- *Translated by Lily Yougie*

Rainforest, open forest, mangrove/beach forest and swamps have different bush tucker in different seasons *(Figure 2)*. Rainforests have plenty of fruits-we eat around forty different types, mainly in the dry season. In the wet season, rainforests are rich in tree nuts, like *barka*, *bujabay* and *bijalambay*. Many of the rainforest nuts we use are only found in the wet tropics. In the old days, *marra* was our main plant food in the dry season, and is found in open forest. Yams grow on the beach side and on the rainforest edges, *wukay* is the main one.

The fringing reefs and beaches give us shellfish all year round (*Figure 3*). We also catch many reef fish, and turtle, especially when the sea is flat. The moth larvae *burngu* is a delicious food but it is hard to find nowdays. On the inland side, the rivers are alive with eels, freshwater fish, and turtles. We also catch wallaby, porcupine, bandicoot, goanna and other small animals. Scrub turkey eggs are very good bush tucker.

Top Left: *Eileen Walker displays marra.*

Top Right: *Eileen Walker and Doreen Ball digging for Bulkiji on Weary Bay*

Bottom Left: *Sonya Doughboy digging jarruka eggs, Cedar Bay (Mangkalba). (Photo: R. Russell).*

Bottom Right: *Bulkij found in the sand.*

December
barka, bijalambay, bi
nuts from mad
NUTS SEEDS
banday, bungal, dukunjal
some fruits ripen
FRUITS
ROOTS YAMS
SHOOTS LEAVES
FIRES
can kill y
November
October
September
August
July
bininji, bunduru, durral, dukunjaka, jajikal, janbal, jarramali, jungka, kalbariji, kurruy, maraja, marrku, mukukanka, ngurrkul, walkaran, wanakan, warkul
main time for many different fruit trees
marra
harvesting of marra nuts in the ngalkalba forest
dangerous time for fires
can kill fruit trees in the madja,
main fires time for cleaning grass in open forest
easy walking to collect marra
freshwater lily fruits, tubers, stems, stalks available
found in freshwater swamps
al, bungkay, djinjur, jula, kalkut, kawu, warrabuka
off yam vine, wakay is nice & floury, after that new yam vine
dness from the old root
angka, mili, mujari, yirrngkunji

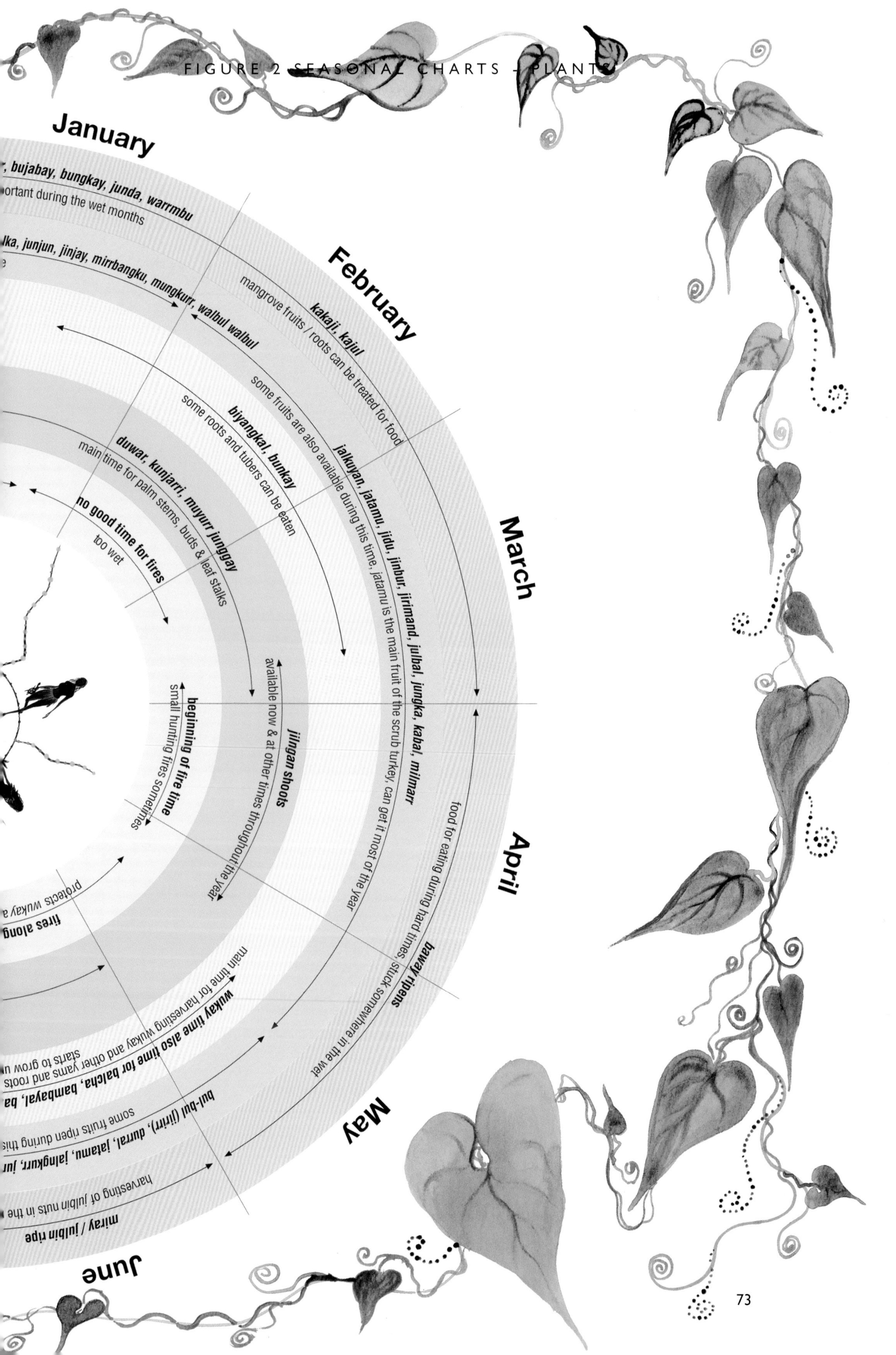
January
bujabay, bungkay, junda, warrmbu
during the wet months
junjun, jinjay, mirrbangku, mungkurr, walbul walbul
February
kakaji, kajul
mangrove fruits / roots can be treated for food
jalkuyan, jatamu, jidu, jinbur, jirimand, julbal, jungka, kabal, milmarr
some fruits are also available during this time, jatamu is the main fruit of the scrub turkey, can get it most of the year
biyangkal, bunkay
some roots and tubers can be eaten
duwar, kunjarri, muyurr junggay
main time for palm stems, buds & leaf stalks
no good time for fires
too wet
March
jilngan shoots
available now & at other times throughout the year
beginning of fire time
small hunting fires sometimes
April
baway ripens
food for eating during hard times, stuck somewhere in the wet
fires along
protects wukay
wukay time also time for balcha, bambayal,
main time for harvesting wukay and other yams and roots
starts to grow
May
bul-bul (jirirr), durral, jatamu, jalngkurr,
some fruits ripen during this
miray / julbin ripe
harvesting of julbin nuts in the
June

December
November
October
September
August
July
balarri, barball, dawal, jarbir, jirrjirr, kudi, ngalkun
many different kinds of reef & estaurine fish are fat & good to catch at this time
eggs of the wabul bird, also jamarbina, nyili-nyili
torres strait pigeon eggs are available while they nest on the off shore islands, magpie, goose and duck eggs in the swamps
diwan eggs
scrub turkey nests at the same time as (bilngkumu) crocodile, good to eat diwan
jarruka eggs
time to collect eggs & later on young chickens from the scrub fowl
jarrabina (tree kangaroo) ready anytime
jarramali, burns - bring wallabies to
fires can be dangerous at this
badibu, bilmbin, yawu
best months for catching various types of stingray, shovel-nosed shark, flathead
good time for kambi
flying fox is ready from July through to November
binbarrbay, darrba, karda, kulngu
best time for hunting wallabies, kangaroos, bandicoots & other small anamals
year round but care is needed at breeding time, kurriyala liver is very good to eat
honey, can be collected - best in the flowering season, & just before the wet season, when the bees stock up on honey
main time for hunting fires
large wallaby drives in the old times
warra, kiju, marbu, markabina, nikar, nga-ngal, ngarrakaja, yulba
but can also be collected throughout the year, sea urchins, crabs also fat
dandarrbina, julaji, kubarr, kuyu kuyu, ngujay
kinds of freshwater fish, eels & turtles can be caught
balarri, jalkay, midirr
queen fish & cooktown salmon & butter fish

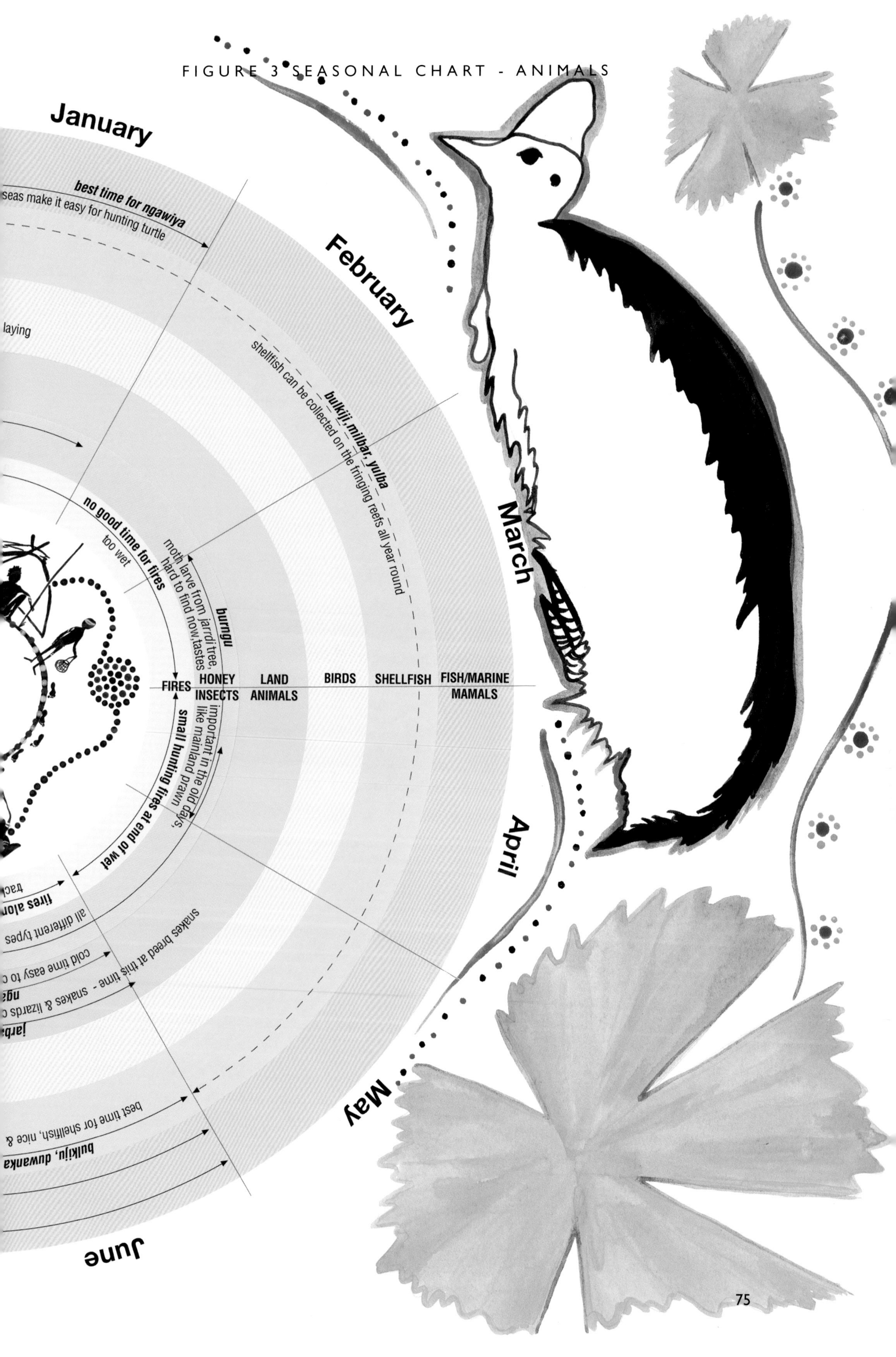
January
February
March
April
May
June
best time for ngawiya
seas make it easy for hunting turtle
laying
bulkiji, milbar, yulba
shellfish can be collected on the fringing reefs all year round
no good time for fires
too wet
burngu
moth larve from jarrdi tree,
hard to find now,tastes
important in the old days,
like mainland prawn
small hunting fires at end of wet
FIRES
HONEY
INSECTS
LAND
ANIMALS
BIRDS
SHELLFISH
FISH/MARINE
MAMALS
snakes breed at this time
all different types
cold time easy to c
snakes & lizards c
best time for shellfish, nice &
bulkiju, duwanka

Walu-yindu Walu-yindu Baya, buluriji/wungariji

Ngalku ngulkurr mayika minyaka jambulingkaku. Nganjin ngalku wajul wuljaljidaku yala-yala jakalbaku nganjin wajun wawu kambarmun. Nganjinanga ngalku kari yalbay. Yinya ngananga kari Law. Yundu kari ngalku waju yinya bubu yunu kari yinduymbu bamanga bubu. Charlie Denmanangka balkan:

Bamangka ngalku kari yalbay yarrku wajul yala 2 or 4 acres. Jana buban wajul jilbaka baljinka dunganka wanjabu jana minya manil. Yinya junjuy-junjuy wajujida (12 November 1995, Mossman).

Ngalku nyulurrku wajuji kunbay, nguba yinya bubu duna nguba kulji-kulji. Buluriji ngalku karangkaldarr madjanga-wajuji mayi yam kujil-kujil juma-jumaka kadaramu murun nyajil ngalkungu dulinga. Jana binga-binganka kamba-kambanka dunganya madjanga kawal yirrkanya "choonk choonk" yinilbunganya kadar kanbal binga-binga jana kalkajikuda, Janjanarinya, minya kadar wandirikuda jurrbuku jikanka dakarinya:

Yundu buban baya wajul, minya kadar julmbanumu bundarinka yinyay. Yundulu dungan dunganji-bajalu nubijinji bajalu jananda. Balu jananku kadarika yunuduku, yundu kari dungay nubijika junjuy-junjuyngku jana kaday baja jikanka jirakalka (Peter Fischer, 5 December 1995, Buru) *- Translated by Lily Yougie*

Top Left: *Flying Foxes (kambi) are a good feed for those who hunt them with boomerang (wangal).*

Middle Left: *Open country near Weary Bay harbours wukay.*

Bottom Left: *A close up of a wukay plant. (Photo: R. Hill).*

Different fires, different seasons

Fires are important for both plant and animal bush tucker. We light fires all year round from when the grass will first burn at the end of the wet season. Our fires are not very big. Under our Law, you can't let a fire burn across from your clan estate to somebody else's country. Charlie Denman explains:

Bama burns, not much, they burn 2 or 4 acres, where they could walkabout, camp, where they could catch the minya.... now the whole thing gets burnt (12 November 1995, Mossman).

Fires generally are allowed to burn up to a place where they stop naturally, perhaps because the ground is wetter or rocky. In the cold time, fires along the edge of the scrub help save the yam crop from getting burnt later in the year. Wallabies' tracks can be seen on the ground burnt in these fires-our old people used to go into the scrub and call "choonk choonk", frightening the wallabies out to the men waiting with spears. Animals are also attracted to fresh shoots after a burn:

You burn a little patch, for wallabies and kangaroos to live on, instead of you hunting them, they'll come to you, you don't go hunting things, they come to young shoots of grass (Peter Fischer, 5 December 1995, Buru).

Top Right: *Edward Barney and Roy Gibson.*

Middle Right *A small patch fire in the late wet season. (Photo: R. Hill).*

Bottom Right: *Peter Fischer. (Photo: R. Hill)*

Wungarijida marralda ngalku wajukuda- ngalku wajul kadarangka, mayi marra mujanka. Ngadingadiku binga-binga murumanya nyubuninya baya wajunya kanbalda binga-binganka birrabu bubu kulbal-kulbanya, kadar kanganka jinbal kanganka kalkabudamanka. Jana kamba-kambangka yalarrku birrabu bubu-kulbanya.

Yundu mumbarabuku yala yundu wajul ngalku wungariji jarramaliji-ngalku dakal wangkar wuburrdurr yala madjanga, mayi yam wajujida. Ngalurimundu buyun damal kulji ngujakuramun bubu. Ngadi-ngadiku bayan bamanga jikan, bayan ngananga wajujinji ngananga karrar jirray bayanka. *- Translated by Lily Yougie*

Top Left: *David Buchanan performing at the Laura Cultural Festival.*

Top Right: *Country near Roaring Meg.*

Top Left: Edward Barney displays a nut-cracking rock.

Top Right: Fire near Mossman.

The early dry is the main fire time-burning used to be mainly for wallaby hunting and making it easy to go out and collect *marra*. In the wallaby drives of the old days, all the men would stand in a circle, some lighting the fire, and others beating on the ground with branches, forcing the wallabies to run for a gap where they would be speared. The women would sometimes help with beating the branches.

You have to be careful when you burn in the late dry and storm time-fires can climb the mountains and kill our fruit and nut trees in the rainforest, and kill our yam crops. Hot fires can also damage rocks that are very important parts of our story places, our sacred sites. In the old days, our camps were thatched with grass, so we had to be very careful not to burn our camps, and also to have plenty of grass for making our *bayan*.

Ngalku ngulkurr jarramaliji kadar wandi manil jikanba jurrbungu. Ngalku kari waju buluriji jamar kidanka madjanga. Ngalkubu buyun damal:

Ngalku wuljaljiku wujun-wujuji, wujun-wajujiku wuljaljiku...Yundu buyundamal madja ngulkurrmunku, wanjabu yibuy dakal-dakanya (Peter Fischer, 5 December 1995, Buru).

Nganjinanga yinya juku jimal bayaka wajunku. Nyiku-nyiku nganjin matches usimbungal yala drip torch. Nganjin wawu kari jirakalka yanyu junjuy baya pellets helicopterbu daraymanil-malin- yundu bubumunduku kuku yirrkay yirmbalba, jawunkarranda, yundu ngalku wajunku.

- Translated by Lily Yougie

Left: *Late dry season burn at China Camp. (Photo: R. Hill).*

Fire can be good at storm time for bringing wallabies onto the green pick. Sometimes a low cool fire can be used to clean up the undergrowth in small patches of *madja*. Fires can also ruin rainforest:

Fire seems to keep burning more trees, and more trees.... you spoil the beautiful walking scrub, where the lawyer vine supposed to be growing (Peter Fischer, 5 December 1995, Buru).

We have special sticks for lighting fires, *jimal* from a few different trees. Nowadays, we can use a match, or a drip torch. We don't like the new way of lighting fires by dropping fire pellets from a helicopter - you need to be on the ground to talk to the story, and the old people on country, when you light a fire.

Top Left: *Black Palm (ngakan) is important for dilly bags (balji) and nets.*

Top Right: *Red Tulip Oak, (wuymbariji) in Mossman Gorge.*

Marra, Wukay yala yindu mayi kanbal balkal balkal

Marra nyunbun jurrbu wawu ngalkuku:

Marra jurrbu wubulmal ngalku ngulkurrduku wajul .

(George Kulka (Snr.), 14 November 1996, Roaring Meg).

Yalanji-warra bubungu juku marra warrmbabal janjanay duliburr bunjalbaku, kudamundu madjanga janjanay. Yanu ngalkal, madjaburra kanbin nyiku-nyiku waybala kadan bulkinji, ngalkubu buyun-damal. Nganjin ngalku wajul ngalkalba marra jurrbu balkajinkabaja. Nganjin kari madja wajul, madja nganjinanga kujinka mayiji nganjinanga. Peter Fischer (Challa /Jinkarr) balkan:

Madja, yundu ngalku wajul-wajul, yundu madja buyun-damal.... yundu buralku waju, yanyu, yundu bubu nyajil yarrku, ngananga ngalkal kari yalbay (19 June 1996, Buru). *- Translated by Eileen Walker*

Top Left: *Marra seeds growing in open forest on the banks of the Bloomfield River.*

Bottom Left: *Eileen Walker holding marra seeds.*

Marra, Wukay and other Tucker for Processing

Marra is one plant that likes fire:
More (marra) seeds come with the right time fire.
(George Kulka, 14 November 1996, Roaring Meg).

In *Yalanji* country, stands of *marra* trees are often found in patches of open forest surrounded by rainforest. Some of these patches of open forest have grown over with rainforest trees since *waybala* came with their cattle, and changed the way we run fire on our country. We burn open forests to help keep the *marra* productive. We don't burn the rainforest down, we have to look after the rainforest because it also has many important foods. Peter Fischer explains:

The madja country, if you putting them hot fires, you knock off the scrub.... you just burn a patch, like here, you can see the country, our (open) forest pockets is not very big (19 June 1996, Buru).

Right: *Eileem Walker climbs a cycad tree together marra seeds.*

Top Left: Doreen Ball crushing marra seeds.

Top Right: Kathleen Walker, Eileen Walker and Doreen Ball with a harvest of marra seeds.

Marra mayi nyunbun nganjinanga ngujakuramun. Jalbu Yalngkurr, jakabamun marra-daman balkan yalarrku mayi yam bakan (McConnel 1931). Jalbu-jalbungku mayi marra daman. Ngalba-Yabangka balkan:

Marra ngujakuramun, ngadimunku. Marra jalbu-jalbumu. Bula ngalbabulanka marra daman. Nyulu Junbirrangka bulanda ngalbabulanda milbin wanjarr marra damal. Kalkarubarrangka bulanangan ngalbabulal kangan wukurrin wangkar-wangkar madjaburr manjaldarr. Bula nyiku yinyaykuda bundanday, babarr/ jinkurr ngalbabulal (31 October 1996, Thompson Creek).

Kumarkaji yinyaykuda Yalanji- warra jalbu-jalbu wubulku muruman mayi marra damal-daman. Jana jalbu-jalbu jinalinga bundandan marrakuda nyurrbal-nyurrban wungar kalbaymundu, nyubun jalbu bajaburrngaya yinduynju maninya. Jananda mayi marra nyiduburrkuda. Kumara yinya kuku balkal nyanday marramun, yinya bananga yilbanya bulanga nyujayanga/kuyumu dajinya. Kaji, yinya bulawukuda mayi dambakuda dingkal (George Kulka (Snr.), 19 June 1996, Buru) .- *Translated by Eileen Walker*

Above: *Different stages in the processing of marra.*

Marra was one of the most important foods in traditional society. *Yalngkurr,* an eaglehawk/woman, made the first *marra*, and also dug the first yams (McConnel 1931). Women have responsibility for *marra*. Dolly Yougie explains:

Marra comes from the Ngujakura, from the beginning of time. Marra is a woman's thing. The two sisters, they made marra. Junbirr, the skink, taught them how to make marra. Kalkarubarr the snake chased those two sisters away up into the rainforest mountains. That's where they sit now, Ngalbabulal, the two sisters (31 October 1996, Thomson Creek).

Kumarkaji is a place where large numbers of Yalanji women would make marra. The women would sit on the rocks, grating all day; when one was tired another would take over. They would be up to their waist in marra. Kumara is the word for the coarse particles left over from the grinding, which would be thrown into the water to feed turtles and fish. Kaji the fine fraction, was used for flour in dampers (George Kulka (Snr.), 19 June 1996, Buru).

Yalanji maral-maral binalman kamba-kambadamun wanjarr marra, wukay damanya. Yinya marra buyun, yundu kaka dama mubarabuku. Wukay nyama janimal, bananga ngaba yinyamun balnjinda yijarrika dingkada dubalba yinyamun banabu damal-damada. Marra bayanga waju yinyamun dumbul kida bananga ngaba duda dirkabunga-dirkabunga banabukuda julurrika kakakuda yunganka.

Yinyarrin Yalanji-warranga bamanga mayi bujabay, bungjay, junda, miray, julban, wukay, baway, biyangkal. Bujabay madjaji bamanga nyubun mayi ngadimunku. Bujabay juku yalbay madjanga ngalku kari waju yubaku, yinya juku ngalkubu wajul, yinya juku buyun damalkuda.

Above: *The collection of wukay is a woman's role in Yalanji culture.*

Yalanji girls learn how to prepare *marra* and *wukay* from the older women. It can be dangerous, and must be done properly. *Wukay* is boiled, crushed and washed several times to remove the poison. *Marra* is roasted, peeled, soaked, crushed, sieved, and washed many times to remove the poison.

Many plants used by *Yalanji bama* in traditional society required the same sort of processing to remove poisons: *bujabay, bungkay, junda, miray, julbin, wukay, baway, biyangkal*. *Bujabay* nuts were the main ones from the *madja* for food in the old days. *Bujabay* is a large tree that has to be protected from fire - if fire damages the bark, rot will get in and spoil the tree.

Above: *Wukay is a nutritious food. Today the practice of collecting and preparing wukay continues.*

Top Left: *Red Lacewing butterfly.*

Top Right: *Lesueur's frog.*

Bottom Left: *Stinging tree plant (mili). (Photo: Ing Toh).*

Bottom Right: *Coopers Creek.*

Left Page: *Lowland fan palm forest (muyurr).*

Binalmal Ngalkuku Yalanjinka

Yalanji-warra binal nganawunku bubuku janakuda marri-marri kamba-kamba/binga-binga kuku dajin kujinka, nyiku jana maral-maral warru-warru nganjin muruku dungay bubungu. Jana yarrka-yarrka binalmal kunkun bungal-bunganya yalarrku mara dajil minya mujanka yam bakanka, yulba, bulkiji, marbu, juwarru yala wanjarr baya wajul, jana kukungu milkajanay nganjinanda.

Above Left: *Agnes Burchill sharing stories with our children.*

Above Right: *Marianne Port demonstrates to her daughter Shannon, how to draw a crocodile .*

Nyiku yarrka-yarrka dungay schoolbu binalmanka, yinyaynka murumanka (NAIDOC) ngulkurr nganjinanka yarrka-yarrka wundinka jilba junjuy-junjuy mayi milbinka mujanka. Nganjin nyajinka nganjinanga yarrka-yarrka nyajinka binalmanka milka wulanji nganjinangkamunku Yalanjimunku ngujakuramunku:

Nganjin yarrka-yarrka, wundinka jilba madjanga, jana binalmanka madjaka, balnjika, janjil, bural balnjika warrmbabunganka, mayi milbinka wanyu mayi nukanka nguba ngulkurr nguba buyun (Bobby Yerry, 30 April 1996, Zig Zag homestead).

- Translated by Kathleen Walker

Learning about Fire the Yalanji Way

Yalanji knowledge about our country is passed on from the older generations to the young ones mostly through going out into country together. Children learn by watching and helping us collect shellfish, dig yams, light fires, and listening to our stories.

Above: *Mossman children performing at NAIDOC week celebrations in Mossman.*

Today our children spend a lot of time in school-so we make sure we use school time, like NAIDOC week, for cultural activities. We would like our young people to pay more attention to *Yalanji* knowledge:

We want to take the kids away, take into the bush, let them learn the bush life, camping out, swimming, finding a good camp, eat this one, this one dangerous don't eat it (Bobby Yerry, 30 April 1996, Zig Zag homestead).

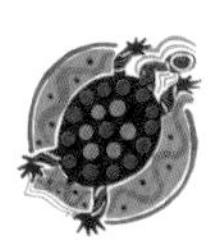

Nganjinanga Yalanji-warra wubulbajaku junjuy-junjuy nganjinanga kuku ngujakuramun kujinka. Bamanga Bubu Ngadimunku (BBN) Community Rangers Kubidi kuku balkal-balkal University yalarrku TAFE studentsanda, yala kanbalanda Yalanji-warranda bamanda. Jana BBN Rangers yalarrku kanbalnji maja-maja bubuku yala kanbal agencies. - Nganjin binalda nyajinda junjuy-junjuy yala kulji barka dudal-dudan, kulbanmuku (stone axe), buralba. Bula TAFE and Schoolangka dajin jananda Rangerda Kaban burri "Caring for Country" Programs wanjabu bama/waybala binalmanka yala balkawanka Yalanji Kuku. Wujal Wujalangka, kuku junkurrjiku kujil yinyay ngananga Yalanji Kuku Groupangka.

Kuku-Yalanji Dreamtime Tours yalbay junjuy-junjuy Gorgemunbu jana ngarrbal-ngarrbalanda milbil-milbil ngujakuramunbu bubungu. Nganjin julngkaji yala wara wuri kukuku nganjinanga ngajukuramunku.

- Translated by Kathleen Walker

Top Left: *Eddie Baird is a guide at Mossman.*

Top Right: *Art at the Cultural Camp.*

Bottom Left: *David Buchanan. (Photo: R. Hill)*

Bottom Right: *Adelaide Baird and Harry Shipton. (Photo: R. Hill)*

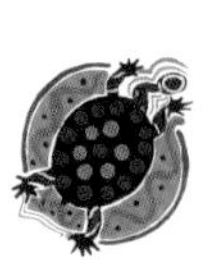

Top Left: *Raymond Buchanan showing rock engravings, used to sharpen stone tools.*

Top Right: *Roy Gibson with a traditional stone knife near Noah Beach.*

We have lots of different ways of keeping *Yalanji* knowledge alive. *Bamanga Bubu Ngadimunku* (BBN) Community Rangers at the Mossman Gorge teach University and TAFE students, as well as other *Yalanji* people. BBN Rangers also do cultural heritage surveys for landholders and agencies - we identify artefacts like nut cracking rocks, stone tools, and other significant cultural sites. TAFE and the Schools offer Ranger and "Caring for Country" Programs where our people can learn and teach *Yalanji* knowledge. At Wujal Wujal, our language group keeps *Yalanji* language strong.

Kuku-Yalanji Dreamtime Tours is a multi-award winning business at the Gorge based on our cultural knowledge of country. We paint and dance our stories and culture.

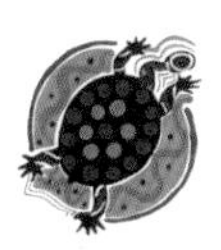

Balkakuda Ngalkuku Bubuku

Nganjinanda Yalanji-warranda ngujakuramun, bama yinyaymun bubuku janaku kuku yirrkay junjuy-junjuynku. Peter Fischerangka maral-maralanda yala warru-warrunda milkabakan ngujakuraka:

Top Left: Eileen and Kathleen Walker point to wukay.

Top Right: Roy Gibson examines a shield tree

Yundu kari dungay ngabaku ngalku waju, yundu majaku bubuku mana, milka janjanay ngalku wajunku (12 November 1996, Buru).

Yundu ngalku wajunku yundu bama maja-maja bubuku murubunga balkawanka. Juma bama kunja kuwa-kuwamun Yalanji-warra yalarrku Nganjin Naka-Nakamun Yalanji-warra.

Ngana balkaway wanja-wanjaku ngalku wajul yinya nguba yirmbar, nguba juljal babajika wanja-wanjaku ngalku wajul. Jana BBN kaban nyajilarr yinyamun bubu walu wukurril. Ngujarkura junkurrji-bajaku ngalkuku. Bama binal-binal yala marri-marri junjuy-junjuy walu wukurril yinyamun yalamal ngalku wajuda.

Jana jikan marabu manil, dirkabal, yinya jikan dirka-dirka bajaku kari ngalku waju baja (Jack Pierce, 16 April 1996 Mossman).

Ngayula wawu dunganka muyariji, yinya ngalku kudamunduku dungay, wajun-wajunji waymbul-waymbulku muyarji, yundu waju madjamunkuna (George Kulka (Snr.), 14 November 1996).

- Translated by Kathleen Walker

Planning for Fires on Country

Under *Yalanji* Law, people with the right connections to country have to make decisions about what happens on that country. Peter Fischer reminds the young ones of the Law:

You can't go and burn without getting the elders, listening to when to burn (12 November 1996, Buru).

So the first step in planning to light a fire is getting all the right people together to talk about it. Sometimes this means bringing other Aboriginal people together with Eastern *Yalanji* people.

We have to be sure about issues like cultural sites, story places, safety, and making sure it is the right time for lighting a fire. The BBN Rangers do surveys for cultural sites first. There are strong *bama* laws about lighting fires. Senior custodians assess the local weather and environmental conditions first:

They pick up the grass, and scrunch it up in their hand, and if it gets too powdery, well it's no more lighting grass (Jack Pierce, 16 April 1996 Mossman);

I like to go against the wind, the fire sort of goes backwards, burning against the wind, you start him from the scrub (George Kulka (Snr.), 14 November 1996, Roaring Meg).

Top Left: *Edward Barney and Roy Gibson observe a fire.*

Top Right: *Traditional stone knife near Noah Beach.*

Above: *Eddie Baird and rock-art in Mossman Gorge.*

Kanbalba bubungu, ngalku waju wangkar-wangkarmundu yinyamun ngaluri waymbulku bada walal-walal, ngalkubu kari buyun damal madja.

Kari jikan waju bada-badamundu ngalku yunga yarra wangkar wuburrdurryundu wangkarmunduku waju,ngalku balu wambulku bada wala. Juku kari wajuji. Yundu bada-badamun wajul ngaluri yala wangkar dakal juku wajuji muyarangka dakamanilbaja wuburrdurr. Ngalku wawu kari walanka kankuburr, yala waymbulku wajun-wajunji yala mosquito coil (Peter Fischer, 12 November 1996, Buru).

Nyiku ngana binalmal jirakalmunji junjuynji yala Geographic Information Systems balkanka wanjarr/wanjabu ngalku wajunka. Ngalku kanbal kulijimal buyun yala, yinya ngalku ngulkurrduku binaldaku waju. Kanbal nganjin binalmal yinyanka Level One Fire Officers, nganjin yalarrku junjuy-junjuy ngalkuku kujinka yala kambi ngalkuku didan wajunji.

Wawu ngalkumun yundu dungay duli nyaka. Eddie Madsen, Yalanji-bama bubuku maja binal ngadi-bajaku bulkinka, nyulu balkan:

Yundu ngalku wajuda, yala dungay baja bubu walu wukurrika baja duli, yala warngku kulurmal bubu nyakabaja bubu wanjarrmalmal. Yundu dungay baja nyaka baja wanjabu bulki nukan-nukaji (6 May 1997, Buru). *-Translated by Kathleen Walker*

Above: *Edward Barney above, and Lizzie Olbar left, learning Geographical Information Systems on computer. (Photos: Paul Dymond).*

In some places, fires must be lit from the top of the hill and slowly trickle down-otherwise they can climb the mountains and kill off some *madja*.

Don't light the grass from the foot of the hill, send the fire up the hill, you gotta burn on the top, let the fire come down slowly. Won't hurt any tree. When you burn down the bottom, the flame go to the big tree, nearly kill everything on the front of the fire, the wind push him up the hill. Fire don't like going down the hill, just slowly going down like a mosquito coil, burning down slowly (Peter Fischer, 12 November 1996, Buru).

Today we are starting to use modern tools like Geographic Information Systems to help us plan for fires. Fires can be very dangerous and safety is important. Some of us have trained as Level One Fire Officers, and use fire safety equipment and protective clothing in the field.

It's important to go back and look at what happens after a fire. Eddie Madsen, a *Yalanji* traditional owner with extensive experience in cattle, explains:

You've really got to burn, and actually go back, maybe every fortnight or something, and check the country, so you actually see the change, somebody's got to actually go back there, and find out how many cattle are eating off the burnt country (6 May 1997, Buru).

Ngananga Bubu Daya baja (Nganjinku Bamanka Ngulkurrduku Kujinka)

Ngananga bubu, yalarrku ngananga bama wawu kujin-kujin manubajabuku jana waybala yaluy kadan. Yarraman, bulki wudin bubungu Yalanji-warra bama kiril-kiril ngalku wajunku, madjangka ngalkal kanbinkuda. Mayi marra, wukay kunbarinkuda ngalkal madjabu kanbin. Yanu bubu nganjin wajunkubaja, bunjal kidankabaja yala ngadi-ngadimunku. Baya ngalkubu madja bunjal kidan Yalanji bubu mayi nandangka.

Jana madja nyandal-nyandan, yinyamun jana baya ngalku wajul, ngara yalarrku wajun, Jana minya jiba badi-badiku dunganda bubungu yinduymbu, nyulu jarrabina, walkarr, jana wubulku dunganda (Lizzie Olbar, 28 May 1996). *- Translated by Francis Walker*

Above: *Recently cleared rainforest in Yalanji country.*

Bringing our Country Back

Our country, as well as our people, has suffered a lot since *waybala* came here. Bringing the cattle and horses onto the country, and not letting *Yalanji* run the fires properly, has caused areas that were open forest to be covered over with rainforest. Bush tucker like *marra* and *wukay* disappears when these areas become thick with vegetation. We would like to burn some of these areas again and bring them back to open forest. In other places, fire has been used to help clear the forests of the *Yalanji* homelands for agriculture:

When they start cutting down the rainforest, they light a big fire, burn the stumps to get rid of them, and the poor animals have to go for another place to live, the climbing kangaroo, goannas, all leave (Lizzie Olbar, 28 May 1996, Jajikal).

Top Left: *Rainforest canopy.*

Top Right: *Forest dragon.*

Above: *Logging near Shipton's Flat*

(Photos: R. Hill).

Wawu yinyamun madja bunjalban junjuy-junjuy jurrkijida:

Yinyay Julaymba, yalbay madja, minya wabul yinyay, wabul wubulbajaku yinyay, nyiku jana waybalangka juku nyandan daraminkuda. Jana minya wabulnga juku mayiji yamba karida, Jana wabul kadari yala jana warri baja mayi yamba kari jananga nukanka. Juku ngulkurr mayiji jananga yamba karida bubu bunjalkuda. Ngayu binal kari wanyurrinku jana juku wubulmanjalku nyandan, yinyay wulbul manjaldarr, Yamba jananga juku mayiji bubungu balambaku (Jack Pierce (Wambi), 19 April 1996, Mossman);

Bulingka kimabungan bubu, yinyamun farmerangka dozer wundin, kambar yalbay kadan bubu kima wurarmun julurrin (Peter Fischer, 6 December 1995, Roaring Meg).

Miningka yalarrku ngananga bubu buyun daman:

Jana bubu janjarrin bajaku, buyun-daman, buyun, bubu bakan, karrngka-bungan, yinyakudabi minersangka bakan, nganjin Bama wawu kari yinyayka yinya nganjinga yirmbal buyun-daman (Jimmy Smith, 27 November 1995, Wujal Wujal).*- Translated by Francis Walker*

Top Left: Bloomfield River.

Top Right: Palm detail.

Many changes follow after the clearing:

In the Daintree, big scrub, used to be pigeons, there were stacks of pigeons.... now they knocked all the trees down, now the pigeons haven't got any trees to feed on, they fly in and fly out again, nothing there for them to eat, good trees are all gone from the clearing, I don't know why they cleared so much, there's plenty on the hills, but the food they eat is mainly down on the flat country (Jack Pierce, 19 April 1996, Mossman);

The cattle, soften the top soil, and the farmer put the dozer in, and the big wet takes all the top soil away (Peter Fischer, 6 December 1995, Roaring Meg).

Mining has also damaged our country:

It's changed, wrecked, they just wrecked the place, dig under, make a tunnel.... what the miners done, bama don't like it that way, that's our sacred place (Jimmy Smith, 27 November 1995, Wujal Wujal).

Above: *Brenda Solomon and Zoe Burchill.*

Nganjin bubu ngulkurr-bunganka baja. Yinya Yalanji - warranga, nganjin kuku yirrkay nganjingan bubungu, nganjinaga jawun-karranda, yirmbarba, ngujakuranda, bubu nganjinaga kujinka baja. Bubu yalarrku balkaway ngajinanji. Jana minya janaku kuku balkaway, yamba ngajin binal wanyu jana yalamalmal. Juku, ngaka, yalarrku minya balkaway nganjinanda Yalanji - warranda Bamanda wanyu mayi/minya junjuy-junjuy balkajinda nukanka.

Yinya nganjin jilba dungay nganjinanda bubungu, wawunku nyajil yinya wawubu balkalda. Nganjin kuku yirrkay jawun-karranda. Nganjin balkaway birranda, jukungu, dikalanda, madjanda, yalarrku jalunbu. Jana nganjingan ngulkurrduku kujinka (Judy Shuan, 5 December 1996, Whyanbeel).- *Translated by Francis Walker*

Above: Brenton Missionary.

We want to bring our country back. In the *Yalanji* way, we talk to the country, to the old *bama*, to the stories and the story places, to the ancestral beings, to look after the land. The country also talks to us. Animals have their own language, and can understand each other, even though we may not understand. Trees, flowers, and animals all talk to *Yalanji bama* about the right time for activities on country:

When we walk on the earth, we can feel the spirit.... We must speak to the bama there. We speak to the leaves, trees, plants, birds, the rainforest in the land, or down to the sea. That gives protection (Judy Shuan, 5 December 1996, Whyanbeel).

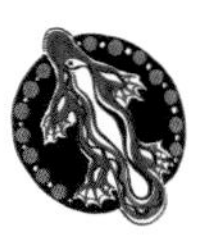

Challa/Jinkarrangka balkal yunu bijarr Buruku:

Ngana bubu ngananga manin-kabaja yala jabalbamunku. Nyulu kadanjiku Captain Cook yaluy, bubu ngadimunku bubu wawu-wawurrku. Nganjin Bama nyubu wawu kari bubu buyun-damanka. Nganjin jibabadi minyaka, ngana bama yalada, nganjin kujinka jananan rirku-rirku. Nganjin bubu nyajinka ngulkurrmanya baja kari yala bubu buyun-damanka baja (20 June 1996, Sycamore Creek).

Yundu nyajin yinya kaya-kaya wubulbajaku , nyiku luriji bikibikingka dungan. Kurranji yamba-kari dungankuda kari kaday baja. Kayangka, jana wukurrinda, Nyulu kari balkan marrkinda kuninka yaluy, yalarrku kaya. Yinyanka, bubu ngulkurr-malbaja yala ngujakaraku, Ngayu wawu nyajinka minya kurranji kadanka baja (12 November 1996). *- Translated by Francis Walker*

Left: *Lester Bloomfield performs the cassowary dance at the Laura Cultural Festival.*

Peter Fischer explains his vision for *Buru*:

We're trying to get the country back the way it used to be. Before Captain Cook came, the country was much different. Black people don't want to destroy the country. We think about the animals, not just the human beings, we want to look after the little things, like frogs. We want to see the country come back good again instead of trying to destroy it (20 June 1996, Sycamore Creek);

You see how many dogs was in that truck today, pig hunters. No cassowary will ever come back. The dogs, they can chase anything away.... he don't let anyone shoot around there, and no dogs. Well by doing that, country'll come back from the dreamtime... I want the cassowaries back (12 November 1996, Buru).

Right: *Cassowary (kurranji).*

Top: *NAIDOC celebrations in Mossman.*

Bottom Left: *Fig tree at Shipton's Flat (Photo: R. Hill).*

Bottom Centre: *Raymond Buchanan at Cape Kimberley.*

Bottom Right: *Looking for oysters (marbu). (Photo: R. Hill).*

Governmentangka nyiku bubu bambal National Parks, junjuy-junjuy bubungu protectedmaninka nganjinandamunbu bubungu, Yamba jana nganjinanda bamandamunbu bubunguu janban-janbay baja. Jana ngajinan kiril-kiril jilbaka yalarrku balnjika.

Jilba nganjingaku, Jana Waybala kaday babaji Yurra wanjarrmalmal, Jana nganjinan bubumunku buyun damal-damal. Jana waybala majamanka, Jana waybalangka bubu buyun damal baja. Jana balu nganjin bamangka bubu buyun damal-damal. Yamba Nganjin Kari. Nganjin wawu jilba dungan-dunganka mayika/minyaka (Jimmy Smith, 27 November 1995, Wujal Wujal).

Nganjin wawu bubu manin-kabaja, nganjin-nganjinku majamanka, nganjinanmunku bubuku National Parksmunku (Adelaide Baird, May 1996, Cowie). *- Translated by Francis Walker*

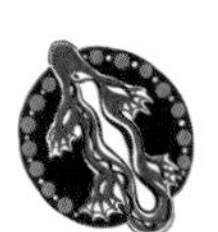

Above: *Weary Bay (Balabay).*

Nowadays the government runs national parks and protected areas on our land, and tries to interfere with our traditional hunting and camping:

Hunting is our culture, they come and tell us what to do, they destroy our culture, they try to take over, wreck the place down again for bama.... they think we're destroying the place. We're not. We're just going out hunting (Jimmy Smith, 27 November 1995, Wujal Wujal).

We want to get the bubu back, we want to be the boss, we want to be the governor of our national parks, on our country (Adelaide Baird, 2 May 1996, Cowie).

Kanbal Marri-Marringa Kuku Ngujakuramun

Yanyu kuku kabanba Yalanji- warra marri-marri binga-binganga yalarrku kamba-kamba ngujakuramun, jana kanbal wulanda. Yalanji- warranga binga-binga, kamba-kamba maja-majakuda, janakuda kuku yirrkay nyiku-nyiku kuku ngujakuramun ngana kari milka wulay. Yanyu kuku kanbalda Yalanji-warra binga-binga kamba-kambanga kuku dajin Ngalkuku. - Translated by Francis Walker

Above: *Elders in Wujal Wujal.*

Nganjin yalanji-warra Bama yaluyku balkajin, bubu ngulkurrbunganka baja. Nyiku-nyiku ngana kuku balkawakakuda, kuku nyajinkakuda, ngujakuramun jakalbamunku. Nganjin yaluy ngadiku kadan, Nganjinan Yalanji-warra kunjal-kunjakuda bubungu ngnjinandamunbukuda. *- Translated by Francis Walker*

Yalanji Fire and the Future

Our vision for the future is to have full control of our country handed back to us, to run our country properly again, to run our own enterprises, to see our children grow up healthy and strong in *Yalanji* culture, well educated and free of problems from grog and violence. Running our own fire management is part of that - we have to burn our country by our Law, protecting all the sacred sites that are connected to the traditional owners.

We *Yalanji bama* were born here and started this country. It's time for us to speak up and be heard, for our Law and culture to come forward. We have been here since the beginning, and our future calls us home to *Yalanji* country and culture.

Right: *Shannon Port at a cultural camp, Cape Kimberley.*
Top Left: *Josh Williams and Wayne Kulka painting in the Mossman Community as part of a TAFE traineeship.*
Bottom Left: *Tiffany George plays in the Bloomfield River.*

Academic Publications from Collaborative Yalanji Fire Research

Hill, R. and Baird, A. 2003. Kuku-Yalanji Rainforest Aboriginal people and Carbohydrate Resource Management in the Wet Tropics of Queensland, Australia. *Human Ecology* **30**, 27-52.

Hill, R. 2001. Collaborative environmental research with Kuku-Yalanji people. In *Working on Country: Contemporary Indigenous Management of Australia's land and coastal regions*, (eds.) R. Baker, J. Davies, and E. Young. Oxford: Oxford University Press. p. 143.

Hill, R., Smyth, D., Shipton, H. and Fischer, P. 2001. Cattle, mining or fire? The historical causes of recent contractions of open forest in the wet tropics of Queensland through invasion by rainforest. *Pacific Conservation Biology* **7**, 185-194.

Hill, R., Griggs P. and Bamanga Bubu Ngadimunku Inc. 2000. Aboriginal Fire Management, Rainforest Conservation and the Sugar Industry in the Mossman District, North Queensland. *Australian Geographic Studies* **37**: 138-157.

Hill, R., Baird, A. and Buchanan, D. 1999. Aborigines and Fire in the Wet Tropics of Queensland, Australia: Ecosystem Management Across Cultures. *Society & Natural Resources* **12**: 205-223

Hill, R. and Smyth, D. 1999. Collaborative Environmental Research with Kuku-Yalanji People in the Wet Tropics of Queensland World Heritage Area. In *Cultural and Spiritual Values of Biodiversity*, (eds.) D. Posey and G. Dutfield. Cambridge: UNEP with Cambridge University Press, pp. 227-233.

Hill, R. 1998. *Vegetation Change and Fire in Kuku-Yalanji Country: Implications for Management of the Wet Tropics of Queensland World Heritage Area.* Townsville: A doctoral thesis submitted in the School of Tropical Environment Studies and Geography, James Cook University.

Further Reading

Anderson, J. C. 1989. Aborigines and Conservationism: The Daintree-Bloomfield Road. *Australian Journal of Social Issues* 24: **214**-27.

Anderson, J. C. 1988. All Bosses Are Not Created Equal. *Anthropological Forum* 5: 507-23.

Anderson, J. C. 1979. Aboriginal economy and contact relations at Bloomfield River, north Queensland. *Australian Institute of Aboriginal Studies Newsletter New Series* **12**: 33-37.

Anderson, J. C. 1984. *The political and economic basis of Kuku-Yalanji social history*. St Lucia: A doctoral thesis submitted in the Department of Anthropology and Sociology, University of Queensland.

Anderson, J. C. 1983. Aborigines and Tin Mining in North Queensland: A Case Study in the Anthropology of Contact History. *Mankind* **13**: 473-98.

Field, D. 1987. *Jakalbaku*. Mossman: Douglas Shire Council.

McConnel, U. H. 1930. The Rainbow-Serpent in north Queensland. ***Oceania*** 1, 347-349.

McConnel, U. H. 1931. A Moon Legend from the Bloomfield River, North Queensland. *Oceania* **2**, 9-25.

McCracken, C. R. 1989. Some Aboriginal Walking Tracks and Camp Sites in the Douglas Shire, North Queensland. *Queensland Archaeological Research* **6**, 103-113.